YOUTH'S CAPTAIN

The Story of Ralph Waldo Emerson

BY

HILDEGARDE HAWTHORNE

ILLUSTRATED BY

W. M. BERGER

LONGMANS, GREEN AND CO.

LONDON · NEW YORK · TORONTO

LONGMANS, GREEN AND CO., INC.
55 FIFTH AVENUE, NEW YORK 3

LONGMANS, GREEN AND CO., LTD.
6 & 7 CLIFFORD STREET, LONDON W 1

LONGMANS, GREEN AND CO.
215 VICTORIA STREET, TORONTO 1

HAWTHORNE
YOUTH'S CAPTAIN

First Edition September 1935
Reprinted November 1935
January 1936, July 1936
September 1936, November 1938
June 1941, November 1943
November 1949

PRINTED IN THE UNITED STATES OF AMERICA

Youth's Captain

YOUTH'S CAPTAIN

The Story of Ralph Waldo Emerson

CONTENTS

ILLUSTRATIONS

YOUTH'S CAPTAIN

The Story of Ralph Waldo Emerson

YOUTH'S CAPTAIN

CHAPTER I

Born to be Educated

A FINE child, Aunt Mary thought him, looking for the first time at her youngest nephew, and though she was sorry for Ruth's disappointment, she herself preferred another boy. Hardly a week old, yet he had the Emerson look, and she smiled, studying the small features of the sleeping infant.

"We'll make a minister of you, my dear," she whispered. "Ralph Waldo Emerson," and she gave each syllable its full value. "It's a good name. May you make it shine among men."

The baby stirred, opened his blue eyes and looked solemnly up at the face bending above him. His aunt nodded slowly, pursed her lips:

"Yes, a worker in the Lord's vineyard. Three boys to educate – brother William will have his hands full!" She straightened, looked out across the cradle through the window at blooming apple trees in the orchard back of the house and the green sweep of meadow. How lovely early June was, and how the various voice of nature, how its ever-changing aspects witnessed the glory of God. *Praise ye the Lord*, she thought. She turned her head at the sound of a step, and as her brother in his black minister's habit came through the open door, she made a slight gesture of welcome. He smiled at her, walked to the cradle and looked down at his son:

"What do you think of the babe, Mary?"

She said nothing for a moment, then, ignoring the question

in a way entirely characteristic, and which her brother recognized with inner amusement, said sharply:

"It's not too soon to begin to plan for his future education. Ruth tells me you are saving nothing out of your salary. I know it is small, but you buy too many books, William. After all, twenty dollars a week is a great deal more than your father ever received. Surely you can lay aside a small sum monthly for the expenses that must be met as the three boys grow up. They must attend Harvard. Think of an Emerson being deprived of Harvard, an Emerson not fitted for one of the professions, and particularly for the ministry! William, would it not be a fine thing if your three sons were all to become ministers? There is room for such pastors as our family has always provided, there is need for them. You know as well as I that the times are dangerous. Too many are affecting to believe that Calvin was too narrow, too hard, are seeking easier ways; indulging themselves in the pleasures of this world without much thought of the discipline required to make them ready for the next. Even you, William—"

"Even I," her brother interrupted, with a hint of impatience. "Even I, because I think this world and this life a fine and fit combination, and see the mercy of the Lord in the friends, the intellectual enjoyments, and the increasing breadth and kindness of our religious outlook that surrounds me, even I am a backslider and that worst of all possible creatures in your eyes, a happy man." He paused, and his eyes too looked out at the June morning, full of color, light and birdsong. "Why, I suppose you think it a weakness to gaze at the charms of such a day as awaits us beyond the walls of the house, would have me close my eyes to the beauty God created—"

"Don't be foolish, William. Look all you want to, but while you look remember that the delight of the eyes is vanity. Nature is beautiful, but nature is only beautiful if it adds to the training of the spirit, lifts the soul to wonder before the power and the majesty of God. I tell you, these Unitarian leanings of yours, this pleasure you find in worldly life, in the society of your friends, this as you call it 'ample and beautiful world,' these are weaknesses you should root out like ill weeds. I know you don't agree, but that shall not prevent my expressing what I know to be true. In any case, all this has nothing to do with what I was saying. These sons of yours, William, were born to be educated; Ralph Waldo equally with John Clarke and William. You should be making provision for this education."

The two had left the cradle and seated themselves now, Mary on a straight-backed chair, William on a settee opposite that permitted him still to look out through the widely-opened window. He was a handsome man, tall and well-made, graceful in movement, with the blue eyes and brown hair of his family. Mary was a small woman, fairer than her brother, quick in motion, with lips that closed tightly and eyes that could flash a blue fire. She looked entirely sure of herself, and so indeed she was.

The young minister frowned at his sister's insistence, his fine profile outlined against the light of the sunny morning. Then he turned to meet her look, that held a touch of scorn, thinking, as he had often thought, that this sister of his, if she would but let other people make their own decisions and manage their own lives, might be a deal easier to live with. He knew her to be warm-hearted and generous, knew that often she suffered remorse for what he privately called her cantankerousness, knew that she was a young woman of wide reading and original thought. But oh, she was difficult, and though she was loved, yet there was always a sigh of relief when she put an end to her visits! She was tireless to work, to help; she was the first to offer assistance in time of need or struggle—but she would not leave you in peace; and she was always in arms for the bitter faith in which she had been brought up, but from which the present-day world was turning toward a new interpretation of the Word of God that was bursting open the prison doors of Calvinism, shaking itself free from the shackles of man-made covenants and written confessions of faith, of endless articles as a term of communion. Yet, when you came down to it, he had more faith in the will of God than she.

This conviction he now proceeded to prove. Turning fully toward Mary he spoke, the rich beauty of his voice, which lent its full share to making him Boston's most popular preacher, rousing in his sister an unwilling admiration.

"I think we can trust Providence, Mary, as we have always trusted in the Divine wisdom. Do you remember how our grandfather Joseph Emerson used to conclude his prayers each night? 'Dear Lord, I crave the boon that no Emerson shall ever be rich.' I don't want to alter that prayer, nor do I believe in laying up riches for the future. The boys must be educated if they are to become the ministers of God. Very well, I believe a way will be found. The salary which I receive I use for the needs of my family – the present-day needs; for charity; and for the forming of a library that will, I sincerely trust, be of vital importance to our city, providing a means of study of the highest value to our young men, and to those scholars through whose work the great teachers of antiquity as well as of later days are brought to the knowledge of the people. John is already at school, though he is only four, and William will begin attending next year, when he reaches three. I see no reason to doubt that Ralph will be less favored when his time to study arrives."

"Very well, William, we'll say no more. But I must be about the housework. In a few days Ruth will be on her feet again and I can go on to Concord. As you know, Mother has not been very well and I can be of some help; she will be glad to have news of the children, and of the new babe."

Mary spoke coldly. She realized that her brother had got the better of her in their argument and felt that natural displeasure we all feel when we see ourselves defeated while still convinced that we are right. Without wasting more minutes she walked briskly out, leaving father and son alone together. William, smiling to himself, crossed the room to a second door, opened it and looked in on his wife, Ruth, where she lay propped on pillows, knitting, in the big fourpost bed.

The two loved each other, and, unlike many New Englanders, were not afraid to show it. Ruth was beautiful in a quiet, dark way. She had in her a great fund of devotion, a strong fortitude, a patience under hardships that was to find plenty of exercise in the days to come, and that had already been proved. Grief too had already come to her in the loss of her little girl Phebe. She had been hoping for another daughter to ease the ache of that loss. But when her husband had asked her whether she were disappointed she shook her head:

"The Lord knows best, William. I did hope for a girl, but this son is needed, I am sure, or he would not have been born to us. Nay, husband, I should think it a sin to grieve because my foolish wish was not granted."

William accepted this statement at full value. He, no more than Ruth, would have adopted a critical attitude in the face of the Divine will. Coming in now he kissed his wife, and not without amusement told her of the little encounter between himself and Mary Moody Emerson.

"For once Mary did not have an answer!" He chuckled, dismissed his sister from his thoughts, and sketched out for Ruth the labors of the day ahead so far as he was concerned. There was to be a meeting with Governor Strong in regard to the plans for the library in connection with the Anthology Club. John Quincy Adams and Daniel Webster would be present. He would probably dine with the Governor after the meeting.

After that there was a business meeting in the vestry of Old Brick, as Pastor Emerson's church was familiarly called. He would hardly be home before the evening meal.

"I have my sermon to write, and there are two funerals to-morrow. One of a woman in childbirth. Ruth, I thanked God on my knees that all went well with you when I heard of that. Of all deaths, methinks that is the saddest."

He was gone, alert, his head high, moving with a pride that his father had chidden in him while he was a mere boy. "William, why do you walk as though the earth were hardly good enough for you to tread? It is not seemly." The abashed boy had hung his head, muttering that he did not know he had shown any pride. He had felt none. He was quite as unconscious still of that proud bearing, that lofty poise of the head which was natural to him.

The parsonage housing the Emersons was a gray, gambrel-roofed building battered by over a century of New England wind and weather, set in the midst of neglected fields and orchards that extended on one side to the brick walls of a row of pleasant gardens, belonging to fine houses where some of Boston's most distinguished families lived in an austere luxury full of dignity and utterly averse from ostentation. In one of these Benjamin Franklin had been born; in another William Hinckley Prescott was later to make his home, and there, in an upper chamber with a lovely outlook, his famous son, the historian, would work at his books, under the terrible handicap of progressive blindness.

A litter of old woodsheds, half-ruined barns, untidy chicken-coops and broken fences in the fields surrounding the parsonage, made this part of Boston a special delight to the poorer children of the South End and Windmill Point. They came there to play rough games with shouts and ear-piercing screams, to fight, to pelt each other with green apples or snowballs according to the season; and to go streaming off in ragged gangs toward the Common, not far away, or the muddy reaches of Back Bay, at the unexpected appearance of a town constable, or the angry yell of some lessee whose cow they had been teasing. The Emerson children used to look on at the doings of these hordes, from behind the palings of the fence enclosing the yard of the parsonage, in mixed fear and envy, much as children of another day regard the mad exploits of circus folk, folk belonging to another, to a strange world, full of perils and wonders. They were of course forbidden to consort with these godless youngsters, and Mrs. Emerson wished that they could be kept from seeing and hearing them; still, this country end of Summer Street was a good place, with plenty of fresh air and a real farm atmosphere for a city; with the cows and chickens, wild flowers, fruit bloom, birds and bees and butterflies of spring and summer, and the long rows of Lombardy poplars and elms that bordered the street.

The Emerson children were not expected to be children. Self-respecting families in those days did not, one might say, recognize childhood. The child was looked upon rather as an empty receptacle, to be filled as quickly as possible with an enormous number of facts, of information, most of it having to do with teachers of the moral law, the ancient philosophers of Greece, and grammar; subjects taught drearily by rote out of dry books compiled by adults who could never have known youth. Indeed, looked at from today, there were practically no young people at the end of the eighteenth and the beginning of the nineteenth centuries. Babies of less than three years were sent to the infant school, where they sat in stiff little rows presided over by sad-faced widows or old maids who kept the switch handy, rebuking even a smile during class hours; and those hours were long. Before infant school the children had already learned their letters at home, not to speak of texts, prayers and

Bible verses by the score. After infant school came grammar school, then Latin school, and when the boys were thirteen or fourteen they were ready for college. Solemn persons of seventeen or eighteen, they taught school in their turn, earning money to help their families or to use for future work in the post-graduate schools of the law, medicine or theology. Schools held throughout the year, a few giving a week's vacation at the end of each quarter, sometimes extended to a fortnight in the midsummer term; but many kept holiday only on New Year's, Fourth of July, Thanksgiving and Christmas. Sunday could not be considered a holiday, since most of it was spent in church, and the rest in religious exercises at home.

In such a world you got your play as best you could, in bits and snatches; usually with the feeling, perhaps not entirely disagreeable, that even that modicum of relaxation was being disapproved of by your elders.

Ralph had been born on May 25, 1803. Shortly after the first anniversary of his birth another son, Bulkeley, was added to the Emerson family. By that time Ralph, a chubby, serious, friendly baby, was trotting about in a funny little dress of yellow flannel, his straight fair hair hanging about his ears; already able to talk, already conscious of discipline. William was now going with John to Mrs. Whitwell's school; but John was almost ready to attend the school for older boys, another short step toward the Latin school. John was five, a thin and delicate child with eyes too big for his face, apt at his studies; William somewhat phlegmatic, good-tempered, taking what learning was forced upon him stolidly but refusing to be pushed.

Aunt Mary came back to take care of the household while Ruth was convalescing. She was full of interest in the new school of English poets who were beginning to attract considerable notice and much criticism. Her brother edited a Monthly in connection with his Anthology Club; in this publication Dr.

John Gardiner, a friend and contemporary of William, had written a paper about this group of writers.

"I want to read these new men for myself," Mary declared. "I have heard praise for these men, but Dr. Gardiner is severe. He writes of Samuel Taylor Coleridge as 'asinine' and of Southey as being full of 'a dull malignity.' I want to make my own decisions."

"I have their books in the Anthology Club Library, and you shall see them, Mary. Wordsworth too is worth studying. The library is growing in a most satisfactory manner; if it grows in the future as it has in the past it will be a collection not to be matched in the entire country."

William spoke truly. The Anthology Library was to develop into Boston's famous Athenæum, an honor to the city and the state, increasingly valuable to succeeding generations of scholars.

Although the weather was warm Aunt Mary found Ralph's small fists tied up in knitted mittens.

"He has a bad habit of sucking his thumbs, and this is the only way I have found for curing him," Ruth told her. "Otherwise he is a very good child, and a loving one."

"He looks more Emerson than any of the others," Mary returned, with her inveterate pride in her stock. "Look at his nose and the shape of his head. Of course they are still those of a baby, but there's no mistaking them. He resembles his grandfather even more than his father."

That grandfather was dead, and his widow had remarried, taking as her second husband Ezra Ripley, the minister appointed to follow the dead man as pastor of the church in Concord. Grandfather William had been a remarkable man, one of the leading scholars of his day, a forceful preacher, a beloved leader of his people. He had built the parsonage close to the North Bridge over Concord River where the Minute

Men had stopped the British advance, the parsonage Hawthorne was to celebrate years afterwards as The Old Manse, and had watched the battle from his own dooryard. For that matter, William had only been prevented from joining in the fight himself by his neighbors, who snatched the musket he had grasped from his hands and begged him to remember that it was not for God's minister to take up arms. Still yearning to be close to the fighters for freedom, he had managed to get appointed the year following to a chaplaincy in the army, going to Ticonderoga, there to catch the prevalent fever and die. He had left, besides his widow, Phebe Bliss, three daughters, one being Aunt Mary, and a son, Ralph's father William.

Mary held her father's memory in the highest esteem. Her feeling that the little Ralph resembled him brought the child close to her heart and fired all her ambition. He too must be a leader, a scholar, a man great in the eyes of his people.

Chapter II

A Child without a Childhood

The Pilgrim and Puritan families who came to New England expected their sons to continue in the trade or the profession of their fathers. It was a merchant family that produced Thoreau, Hawthorne drew from seafaring stock, Longfellow's forebears were mostly lawyers and leaders in politics; but the Emersons were preachers.

To be sure the first of them, Thomas, who had come from Hertfordshire, England, was a baker. He crossed in 1638, determined to have his own way in regard to worshipping his God, and when he settled in Ipswich he named his new house Saint's Rest. He had built it on the slope of Heartbreak Hill, above Labor-in-Vain Creek, so that its name seems like a cry of triumph. He married and had a son, Joseph, whom he dedicated to the ministry. With only one break in the line reaching from him to Ralph Waldo, all were parsons, and all notable.

The first Joseph married the daughter of Peter Bulkeley. Peter was a man of landed estate and considerable property in England, but he gave up everything for the sake of religious freedom and came to the Colonies in 1635. Though he had sacrificed his possessions he kept his taste for leadership and was presently guiding a sturdy band into what was then the wilderness, some twenty miles west of Boston. Here, at a place the Indians called Musketaquid, a spreading valley through which a lazy river drew its shining coils, he founded the village of Concord. This was in 1640. Joseph, coming there to deliver a sermon, met both Peter and his daughter Elizabeth, and very soon afterwards the young people were married. Going to the hamlet of Mendon, where Joseph had been called as the first minister of the newly-settled place, they lived there until an Indian raid wiped out the village and most of the inhabitants. Joseph and Elizabeth, with their young son Edward, escaped with their lives, but with nothing else. They returned to Concord; here they remained for the rest of their existence, Joseph becoming the pastor of the church.

This son, Edward, was the single one in the Emerson line not to take orders. He settled as a merchant in Charlestown, where he proved himself a God-fearing and eminently worthy citizen, was a deacon of the church, and held other positions of trust in the community. He was sufficiently successful in merchandising to be able to send his son, another Joseph, to Harvard College. From this institution the young man graduated with the highest honors, was ordained for the ministry, and kept up his studies to such purpose that he was known through all that part of New England as the Heroic Student. This learned Emerson chose for his wife the daughter of a man also a preacher and only a degree less heroic in scholarship than himself, Mary Moody, after whom Ralph's Aunt Mary was named. The two had a son, William, and great as Joseph's ambition had been for himself, it was even greater for his boy. William was permitted no relaxations from study. From babyhood he was kept at his books, but at last his mother, perceiving that he was growing thinner and paler day by day, decided that it was time to put her foot down. She sent William out to help in the hayfield of their little farm.

Joseph, glancing out of his study window, saw the boy in the sunshine, actually wasting valuable time tossing hay. He called to him sternly, bidding him back to his books. Mary had been waiting for this and she met it firmly.

"It is I, husband, who have told our William he is to work on the farm for a part of every day. If I saw my child's life threatened by the tomahawk of an Indian I should feel it my duty to rescue him at whatever danger to myself. Now that I see his health, if not his life, threatened by an intemperate devotion to books, I can but interpose to the limit of my strength. Temperance, even in the pursuit of learning is, I feel sure, a necessity imposed upon us by the Divine Will."

So William was spared to grow up and become a doughty servant of the Lord. For it was he who was to be Ralph's grandfather and die at Ticonderoga during the Revolution.

It was owing to stepfather Ezra Ripley that Ralph's father, the second William Emerson, entered the church. Coming home from Harvard College toward the end of his senior year he told his mother he preferred either the law or a merchant's career. Sociable and with what he himself described as an "incurable levity of spirit," he felt that he would be better outside than in the church. Phebe was frantic, but her pleas were useless. She retired to her chamber to weep, and there she was discovered by her husband.

The next day, at morning prayers, the Reverend Ezra launched forth into a long, ardent appeal to God Almighty to soften the heart of his stepson and to induce him to lift the load of grief from his mother's spirit by acceding to her natural desire that he should follow the example of those of his family who had preceded him, and become a minister in the service of the Lord. Mr. Ripley was noted for his power in prayer, possessing a native force and eloquence well above the average. At any rate, William yielded to the appeal, became a preacher, and was appointed to the church at a small village called Harvard, some twelve miles from Concord. He had already proved that he could preach a good sermon, and he was distinctly interested in the new spirit that was broadening the teachings of Calvin, and bringing the Unitarian doctrines into favor. He felt that the church was cluttered and deadened by the mass of articles, tenets, rules and regulations under which it labored. He wanted to bring a new liberality into his work. But Harvard was not a promising field. The congregation was stiff-necked; it preferred the old to the new.

Mr. Emerson's stipend, as they called it, was three hundred and thirty-three dollars and thirty cents a year. He could not live on it, even though a yearly load of wood was donated by Squire Kimball, and a leg of pork by Mr. Bromfield, who also gave to the church services whatever color they had. This gentleman's mansion faced the church at the end of an avenue of splendid elms, and down this avenue and up the aisle to his pew, on Sunday mornings, marched the stately Mr. Bromfield, magnificent in scarlet cloak and cocked hat, preceded by his black slave, Othello, and followed by his family. At the end of the services, as he rose to leave, the entire congregation stood up, saluting as he passed. The young clergyman, in the secondhand robes donated by the widow of the parson who had preceded him, cut but an unimportant figure beside Mr. Bromfield.

The fact that young Emerson found it impossible to make both ends meet, that debts harassed him and that, despite his fruitless struggles with them, his congregation remained deaf to pleas for a raise in the stipend, did not prevent his falling in love. In a diary he kept he noted on a certain June day in 1796 that he had ridden out with "the pious and amiable Ruth, and talked with her on the subject of matrimony." Ruth was the daughter of Mr. and Mrs. Haskins of Boston. Her father was an Episcopalian, her mother belonged to the Congregational faith, and the large family of children was divided according to individual preference. William and Ruth had met while he was a student at Harvard College.

Then, as later, William believed that the Lord would look

after His own. After he had brought his wife home to the stony little farm which was the parsonage he set down in that diary of his these brave words:

"We are poor and cold, and have little meal, and little wood, and little meat, but, thank God, courage enough."

It was not until 1799 that the struggle for existence at Harvard village was happily ended by a call to become minister of the First Church, Old Brick, in Boston. Invited to preach there on "the solemn occasion of choosing officers for the Ancient and Honourable Artillery Company," Mr. Emerson, with his melodious voice, his sound scholarship, his grace and dignity, produced so favorable an effect that the invitation followed within the week.

But upon this, Harvard village suddenly found him precious. The congregation could not think of relinquishing him; not, at least, unless Old Brick would pay the parish fifteen hundred dollars! But after some dickering it permitted the transfer at the price of a thousand.

It was a happy outcome for all concerned. The liberality of Mr. Emerson's religious views suited the spirit of his people; his grace and eloquence delighted them. For himself the change was exactly to his mind. He became an important figure among Boston clergymen, was a friend of the governor and a welcome addition to the literary and political circles of the town. His congregation included Boston's best. The one drawback to entire satisfaction, the shabbiness of Old Brick, built in 1713 in a section that had since become crowded, was ended by building a new church on the property where the parsonage stood. At the same time a new parsonage was erected, close to the old one, at the corner of Summer Street and Chauncey Place.

It was on July 17, 1808, that Mr. Emerson, preaching his last sermon in Old Brick, assured his congregation that they "broke none of the laws of Jesus Christ" in deserting the ancient building, "exposed to all the noise and dust of a public street, for one which is remote from the business of the town." On the following Thursday at the first service in the new church, he gave thanks for the change to this "new, beautiful and commodious edifice, where, in the silence of retirement, yet in the center of the territory of the metropolis, we may worship the Lord our God."

There had been changes in the Emerson family before this move. The year after Bulkeley's birth Edward had been born, but in 1807 John had died, too frail to withstand the demands which the Emerson passion for education made upon him. Almost at once after moving into the new house Charles was born, the last boy Ruth was to bear. This made a family of five, William, Ralph Waldo, Bulkeley, Edward Bliss, Charles Chauncey. But of these Bulkeley was not to develop mentally beyond the intelligence of a little child.

William Emerson, though a kind and loving husband and charming socially, was a strict, even a severe, father. He found Ralph far too slow in his studies, rating him at three for not reading better; urging Ruth to take time, if she could, to press him in his studies. During the summer the father led his children to the Bay, where they were thrown into the water and so taught to swim. After his third birthday it was Ralph's turn to join the procession, and he hated and dreaded it. Terrified as the moment approached he used to hide himself, cowering in a corner, but all in vain. His father had little difficulty in routing him out, and into the chill water, choking and gasping, but never screaming, he was tossed, sink or swim. Paddling like a little dog he kept afloat, making frantically for the shore. Discipline, self-control, work; these were the words, these the ideals that ruled his childhood. Of the display of affection there was not a shred, nor the remotest notion that a child had a right to be happy. Years later, as a father, as a grandfather,

Ralph Waldo Emerson was to find his deepest joy in filling the lives of his children and their children with happiness, to delight in their carefree play and laughter. He would watch them, smiling, thinking perhaps of the lost childhood he had known, not bitterly, but with relief that those days were over forever.

The chubby baby had developed into a serious little boy; the yellow flannel dresses been changed for small coat and trousers of blue nankeen – that long-wearing, cheap Chinese cotton the Yankee trading vessels brought back in huge bales from year-long voyagings.

The new parsonage was far more comfortable than the old one, and Mr. Emerson's pay had been increased. But in the autumn after the move anxiety took the place of satisfaction. William fell dangerously ill. The doctor called it a "consuming marasmus." A wasting away, a low fever, probably tubercular. William knew it meant the end, young though he still was. For three more years he continued to work as ardently and almost as steadily as before for his church, his Anthology Club, his library, all the interests he had furthered so effectively and with so much pleasure. He succeeded in completing a history of Old Brick, and attended all the meetings of the Massachusetts Historical Society, and of the Philosophical Society, in both of which he was an important member. Not long before he died, in 1811, writing to his sister Mary, he reiterated that undying faith in Providence which had marked him all his life long. He wrote her that his work in the world was practically over, but that there were plenty of men who could follow him at the First Church and do as well or better than he. He confessed, however, that for his wife and children "my continued presence upon earth is a matter of some moment, as, in the event of my decease, God only knows how they will subsist. And then the education of the latter! But I am not oppressed by this solicitude. Our family, you know, have been so long in the habit of trusting Providence that none of them ever seriously thought of providing a maintenance for themselves and household."

One cannot but feel that a faith which would let William die, regretfully but in peace, leaving behind him a penniless widow and five small children, with a sixth on the way, had a touch of the sublime. The admonishment to take no thought of the morrow could hardly have been more completely carried out. While he lived William had taken care of wife and family. He died secure in the belief that when he was no longer able to provide for them Providence would take up the task.

Nor was his faith unjustified. The congregation that had loved and revered him came to the rescue. Ruth was told that she might go on living at the parsonage for the present, and that William's salary would be continued for a year, after which she would receive a yearly pension of five hundred dollars, for seven years. By then her sons would be old enough to help her.

It was a generous arrangement, and Ruth was touched and grateful. Not only because it solved her immediate problem, but because it witnessed to the feeling for her husband, who had been the joy and the pride of her life. When, presently, the posthumous child was born, and turned out to be the long wished-for daughter, Ruth's grief-stricken heart warmed. The Lord's goodness was infinite.

For his sons the father's funeral was rather an occasion for excitement than grief. Too young to feel the full stroke of death, they could thrill to the pomp of the ceremonial. The church was packed for the service, and sixty coaches turned out to follow the hearse to the burying ground, escorted by the Ancient and Honourable Artillery, in full uniform and playing dirges. It was a stirring ending to the gloom and darkness of the three days after Mr. Emerson's death, and the older boys, William, Ralph and Edward Bliss, returned home with a new sense of importance, to which was added a feeling of responsibility. William, ten, was now head of the house. In the morning he read the prayers, in the evening led the hymns. All three boys helped in the household tasks. Aunt Mary, arriving to be at the deathbed of her brother, remained to assist Ruth in the care of the new baby. The two women talked things over, planning the future. Young William was almost ready to enter Latin school, and hoped to be ready for Harvard in three years.

"He's a fine, sensible boy," Aunt Mary agreed, "a prop to you, Ruth, young as he is. He hasn't his father's brilliance, but he ought to make a good minister when the time comes. He'll have to teach first, though, until Ralph and Edward get through college, and help with his salary. Ralph's inclined to be lazy, I think. I've caught him reading story books when he ought to be studying, and he'd rather recite poems than repeat his lessons. You mustn't allow it, Ruth, really. While my brother was alive his wasting time didn't matter so much, though it's always foolish. Now the sooner he can follow William to Harvard the better."

Ralph at eight was steadily getting taller and thinner. His shoulders sloped and his chest was narrow but he carried himself proudly, as his father had done. His blue eyes were at once gentle and alert, kindling when anything interested him. Then they flamed suddenly, grew intent. He was a sedate boy, never seen to run, never heard to shout, but there was nothing glum about him. His sensitive mouth curved easily into a smile, his voice was noticeably sweet.

"I don't think he's lazy," Ruth protested, in her quiet way. "He's not as John was, studying all the time, pushing himself, but I'm rather glad of that, Sister. My father always insists young people ought not to be worked too hard. Ralph stands well enough in his school classes, except for arithmetic. He doesn't like that."

Mary snorted. Didn't like! What did that matter? It was he high end only that mattered. Harvard demanded mathematics, and she decided she would see Ralph's teacher and suggest that the boy be given special work in that subject. Ruth was a fine, sweet, even a splendid woman, but she was not sufficiently strict.

While Aunt Mary stayed she urged upon her nephews the desperate need to work at their books as they had never yet worked. Every dead Emerson was a reason to shine; the heroic students of the past a summons to be as great, to be greater.

The days of luxury, she told them, were past. From now on they would be called on for self-denial.

"You'll have to learn to give up, to go without! Your mother means to take boarders with the beginning of next year, when Mary Caroline is older. It will mean hard work, and you must be ready to help. But above all you must study. No more laziness, Ralph. No more levity. Everything must be sacrificed to your education if it is necessary, except just enough to keep you alive. Did not the heroes of all ages know how to sacrifice the lesser for the greater? Boys, my dear nephews, learn how to go without material things—mere dust and rubbish," cried Aunt Mary, her eyes alight. "Aim for learning, for dedication to spiritual heights. Be such ministers of the church as these times call for, these backsliding days when men imagine a vain thing, be . . ." and Mary Moody here expressed her conception of the ultimate achievement, "be fit to carry on the name of Emerson, be worthy of those of our blood who have died laboring in the Lord's vineyard."

The boys liked Aunt Mary. She was exciting, and you never knew what she would do or say next. She arrived unheralded, and often, after a storm of wrath because she had been disagreed with, she vanished even more unexpectedly. She quoted from books, she extolled preachers in one breath, and in the next would declare that even the greatest writers or speakers were apt to be mistaken, and that humility would become them far more than pride. Somehow, though she sneered at her nephews if they failed to reach the mark she had set, and fail they usually did for the mark was beyond reach except by a sudden flight of genius; though she scolded if they turned to play a little after hard work; though she snatched from them and hid any book that wasn't a study book; though she laughed if they pleaded they were tired, snorted at a headache, insisted they were quite warm enough without a fire in the room on bitter winter afternoons – somehow, in spite of her fierce spirit and exacting demands, they knew Aunt Mary loved them. Knew too that they could count on her to help them in difficulty, real difficulty. And for a word of praise from her they would toil. Hard won, such a word, honest and worth the having.

The year after Mr. Emerson's death war was declared between the United States and England. Prices were soon rising, while now the sum received by the widow had fallen to the five hundred dollars promised after the first twelve months. Ruth took in boarders, and to save money did all the work with no other help than her sons could give her, between their school hours. Up before six, the two older boys would huddle into their clothes, make the fires in the kitchen and the living room next it. Then Ralph would "set the table for prayers," while William brought in enough wood from the shed to last till evening. Ralph then wakened his mother, who came down to prepare breakfast, while he and William helped the younger children to dress and minded the baby, if she were awake. The little girl was frail and fretful, keeping Ruth in anxiety. After prayers and before breakfast was eaten the mother heard the boys' spelling lesson, a competitive affair at which Ralph was often beaten by William or even by the younger Edward. He wrote Aunt Mary in regard to this that he often "felt angry passions rise in the corner of my heart, for I am sure that this result is won by unfair means."

For a little while before eight, when it was time to go to school, Ruth let the boys play or read. Even those stories of a vain and wasteful sort of which their Aunt Mary disapproved. In the summer they went out into the yard; in the winter they huddled close to the fire. Ralph was now attending the Latin school with William, reading Virgil. Here he stayed till eleven, when he went to a private school taught by a Mr. Webb where he studied the three Rs. At one he and William returned together to find the younger boys already home from their infant and small boy schools. At two they were all back in school, studying hard until five. Back at home errands were waiting for them to do, more wood to be got in, ashes to be taken out. They used to go about these tasks reciting stirring verse together, or they would mimic the voice and accent of a teacher or even a minister. They were cheerful and it never entered their heads to think of themselves as hardly treated. They had never played as other boys played, had always come straight back from school to find more study or duties of one sort or another waiting. No toys had ever come their way. Their food had always been simple, though until now it had been sufficient.

With 1813 the pinch grew more severe. There was only one overcoat not too worn for wearing for both William and Ralph. They took turns wearing it to school while their schoolmates, jeering, would cry "Who goes shivering today?" Once when breakfast, dinner and supper had all been so meager that hunger gripped them to tears, Aunt Mary, spending a week with them, was relating the sufferings of the early Colonists with such fervor and admiration as almost to make them glad they had had practically nothing to eat that day. But when, all unexpectedly, the door opened and Grandmother Ripley entered, bringing a big basket full of eggs, bread, ham and a pumpkin pie, heroism was flung to the winds while the whole family sat down to feast.

The war dragged on. 1814 was worse than the year before. Flour went up to seventeen dollars a barrel, other provisions keeping pace. Ruth could not go on without help. It was decided that the family should go to live with the Ripleys in Concord.

Before the date set for the change little Mary Caroline died.

Ralph, still wearing his blue nankeen, a slender, serious, spiritual-looking boy of eleven, stood beside the small coffin and read the prayers for the dead in a clear sweet voice that did not break, though the tears rolled down his cheeks. Ruth, white and still, took this blow as she had taken the others, without complaint, even without comment. The Lord gave, and the Lord has taken away, blessed be the name of the Lord.

Chapter III

The Wild-eyed Boy, who in the Woods
Chaunts his Hymn to Hills and Floods. . .

By the time he was nine Ralph had begun to write verse of which unluckily only scraps remain. He liked the heroic strain, modeling his lines on such stirring chants as "Warsaw's Last Champion," "Childe Dyring," and other favorites of the day. To the admiration of his brothers he celebrated the naval victories that redeemed for America her reverses on land, especially in New England that had built and manned the gallant frigates, the many privateers, to which these victories were due. It was often these lines that Charles and Edward and he intoned as they washed dishes, set the table and filled the wood-box. And Ralph's spare time was often devoted to composing, a sheet of coarse paper on the table, a stub of pencil in his fist, and that look of abstraction and concentration on his face which was a characteristic throughout his life. As poetry these early compositions had precious little value, but feathers they were that indicated the drift of his genius, the preference for poetry as the means of expression that endured in spite of the popularity of his lectures and his essays. In his own day Emerson was not regarded as a poet, though it was in his poems that the very essence of his thought and his style found form; today it is to these we turn not only to find some of the best and most original of Emerson, but to discover that he was the forerunner of much that is finest in modern poetry.

The Emerson children had visited their grandmother and step-grandfather Ripley at the Old Manse only occasionally. Christmas and Thanksgiving holidays had been spent at the house of Ruth's father and mother, in Boston near them. But Mrs. Haskins had died about the time of William's passing, and shortly after the death of little Mary Caroline Mr. Haskins' life came to an end. The Haskins had been comfortably off, but the family was large and the division of the property gave each of the children only a small inheritance. Ruth received a parcel of land in the city as her share, with certain personal effects. Probably there was some ready money too. At any rate, William entered Harvard this year, and Edward was sent to the Phillips Academy in Andover, where one of the Haskins aunts lived, with whom he made his home. Bulkeley had been placed in the care of other relatives on a farm where he could help somewhat with farm work and live in the open, which best agreed with him. This left only Ralph and Charles to go with Ruth to Concord.

Both boys were delighted. They loved their grandparents—for they thought of the Reverend Ezra in that light—and they adored Concord. Dr. Ripley was a tall, fine-looking man with a patriarchal beard and a noble carriage. He was wise, warm-hearted and simple with a country simplicity; men said of him that he was like some Indian sagamore. Proud of the authority of the church, jealous of his dignity as pastor of his people, stiff in his Calvinism, he was humble as regarded his own worth and gentle to all mankind. The complete Puritan, and among the very last of the old breed, he was not only the leader but the guide and confidant of all Concord, and there was not a man, woman or child he did not know intimately.

The Old Manse itself was a boys' paradise. Ash trees led to it; about it were grouped the outbuildings, the big barn, the chickencoops, the pigeon cotes, dog kennel, the stone pigsty. There was a big vegetable garden where in their season sweet corn, squash, beans, peas, root vegetables, melons and small fruits flourished; hayfields, orchards spread beyond. A gentle old horse and several cows, the dog, a comfortable cat, helped the farm atmosphere. Then there was the river for swimming and boating, the boat a safe, flat-bottomed affair the boys might pull around in at their will.

Here Ralph began to feel that love of nature which would grow to be so vital a part of him as he reached maturity. He delighted to climb the ridge back of the road alone, and sit looking over the fair prospect of lush meadow and dark wood, winding stream and distant hills, breathing the fragrant air, listening to the birds. Charles, who was but little past six, could not accompany him on these scrambles, but Ralph, friendly as he was, liked solitude. To the end of his days solitude was precious to him, a rich and healing tonic to his spirit.

Of course there was school, both lads going to the same institution, where Charles struggled with the beginnings of grammar, learned the multiplication table and read aloud in class, and where Ralph went on with his Latin, began in Greek and read ancient history. He was worried over his mathematics, as always, but he held to a fair average and had no reason to be ashamed of his standing.

One of his chief pleasures was to go driving in the Ripley gig with the doctor as he made his parish calls. His grandfather's talk was full of the meat of life, past and present. He knew the old families and their stories, could tell of pioneer hardships, recall events in the Revolution. He had not been in Concord on that famous nineteenth of April, 1775, but he had heard the detailed account of the affair from the men who had taken part in the fight at the bridge.

"There was your grandfather in his minister's robes, his Bible in his hand, praying to the Lord and watching the advance of the soldiers from afar. As they approached and the first shots

One of his chief pleasures was to go driving in the Ripley gig with the doctor

began to sound, he laid the Book aside, picked up his musket, which he had used in shooting deer and rabbits, and began to run toward the bridge, just as a new detachment of our boys came up the road. It was with the greatest difficulty he was persuaded to return to the women and children waiting at the parsonage. His place, he declared, was in the front rank with his people, whether or no he fired his gun. But at last they got him back, though he refused to enter the house, remaining without, standing straight as any pine tree, and calling aloud upon the Lord."

Ralph, listening, thrilled to the picture. Gradually in the drives and talks, the background of Concord was built up for him; the love for the village founded by his ancestor Peter Bulkeley took deep root. Here was his home, though he did not then realize it; here the spot where he would reach fulfillment and from which his genius would radiate through the civilized world.

Meanwhile the war went on, but the American cause was gradually prospering. Peace came toward the end of February, 1815. A wave of thanksgiving swept the country, and Ralph, bursting with pride and joy, wrote his brother William in Cambridge:

"*My dear Brother:—What a change has taken place in the time since I saw you last, and how happy is that change! But a little while since and the cry of war was heard in every place, but now*

> "*Fair Peace triumphant blooms on golden wings,*
> *And War no more of all his victories sings.*

"*When the news reached this place a smile was on every face and joy in every heart. On the 22d. instant the steeple of the court-house here was illuminated, and appeared very brilliant from this house. . .*

"And now, dear William, with a rhyme I'll close,
For you are tired, I may well suppose.
Besides, we soon shall hear the nightly bell
For prayers – so now farewell."

The stay at Concord, the happy year of wandering in field and wood, chanting aloud the lines he had written or ballads he knew by heart, the country comfort of the Old Manse, was to end. Ruth, now war was over, felt it her duty to live in the city, where Ralph could return to the Latin school and prepare for Harvard. The school's master, Benjamin Apthorp Gould, was a man of exceptional intelligence, an enthusiastic teacher where he found the right material, and he did find it in Ralph, who loved Latin and was beginning to be fascinated by Greek. The opportunity to work under such a man was too valuable to be neglected. It must be good-bye to Concord.

Ralph's schoolmates insisted that before he left he should compose a poem of leave-taking, and recite it when school ended on his last day as a student with them. Nothing loath, young Emerson wrote a lengthy ode which he declaimed from the top of a barrel. It began, with a bow to the schoolmaster and a grin toward the grinning boys:

"I rise to bid adieu
To you, my schoolmates, and, kind Sir, to you,"

and proceeded with many allusions to school affairs and to his mates until the end, where small Charles came in for his share:

"Another brother, small and younger too,
New to the school, and to his studies new,
Hath here received instruction of that kind,
To banish all its dulness from the mind."

There was hearty applause and a good deal of laughter, but Charles sulked. He didn't care for that word dulness and its seeming implication. Many years later Emerson found the old verses and amused himself by reciting them to his own children, who received them with enthusiasm and often afterwards begged for them. Chuckling at the memory of that far-vanished scene, Emerson would stand up and declaim his verses with dignified and appropriate gestures, such as he had used when a boy.

Ruth had been offered a house rent free on Beacon Street, near to where the Athenæum now stands, that noble descendant of the Reverend William's Anthology Club Library. The owner of the house had been called to Europe and would be away for an indefinite period. Ruth was to board the wife and her child as a return, a part of the house being reserved for them. It was not an easy job but Ruth carried it through with a tact and good sense that were admirable. Her sons knew her difficulties however, and Ralph especially was sensitive to them. He loved and admired his mother in the austere New England manner that shrank from any demonstration of affection, any expression in words, but which was deep and lasting under its apparent coldness. Some day he would repay her; some day would make a home for her where she would not need to work nor to worry.

The new house had a yard where a cow given Ruth by Mrs. Ripley could be stabled. Ralph described to Edward the appearance of this yard as follows:

"By boards and dirt and rubbish marred,
Upon the right a wicket gate,
To left appears a Jail of State.
Before, the view all boundless spreads,
And five tall chimneys rear their lofty heads."

The wicket gate led to what was called the Granary Burying Ground, the jail was the county one on Court Street. The letter containing the poem ended with one of Aunt Mary's calls to heroism and notes on study:

"*Aunt's only message is, 'Be Brave;' that is, do not be cast down by thoughts of home. I have begun 'Telemachus' in French at Miss Gale's, and at home I am reading Priestley's 'Lectures on History.' Mother thinks you had better borrow 'Charles XII' or some other history, to amuse you during your vacation.*"

For in such "amusements" the Emerson vacations were passed.

There was plenty of quiet fun in Ralph and not a letter to either of his absent brothers but had its bit of entertaining verse. Even the household tasks were sung, as in this quatrain in another letter:

> "*Melodious knife, and thou, melodious sand,*
> *Touched by the poet-scourer's rugged hand,*
> *When swift ye glide along the scouring board,*
> *With music's voice your happy bard reward.*"

But this fun-making was not the only way in which the boy's talent showed itself. He translated Virgil into such stirring heroic lines that his master, Mr. Gould, kept them to show to the school committee, who were properly impressed. Crossing the Common on a brilliant winter's night Ralph was struck with the glory of the starry skies, standing long to stare and to marvel. Come home, he spent the evening in writing a poem inspired by the bright and darkling vision, which he showed to Gould. The teacher rewarded him with high praise. In his heart Ralph began to dream of being a poet. A minister he was to be, of course. But there was no reason why poetry and the church should not be combined. Had not the Psalmist sung, and hymnals been composed by pastors! But young Ralph's muse neither then nor later turned toward hymn making. The sentimentality inherent in so many of the popular hymns was entirely foreign to his nature.

Ruth had her house rent free, and five hundred dollars' income from the church her husband had served. The cow gave her milk and butter, and, as long as grass was available, was taken to graze on the Common or to the piece of pasture ground Ruth had inherited from her father. Ralph led the beast through the narrow streets morning and evening before school began and after it ended for the day. One morning his mother gave him a dollar and told him to go to the cobbler's and buy a pair of very much-needed new shoes. To his dismay, after tethering the cow on the Common, he found the dollar had disappeared. He must have dropped it. Back he hastened, eyeing every inch of the ground, kicking up the drifted leaves into which it might have fallen. But it was gone, and he had to return to his mother with the news. Ruth, seeing how heartbroken he was, told him not to mind. They would manage the shoes somehow. "We will only hope that whoever found it needed it more than we," she comforted him.

When the two weeks' school vacation arrived next summer Ralph, to his great delight, was allowed to spend the time at the Old Manse. This was in 1816, when he was thirteen. He had done well at his school without being brilliant, and would be ready for Harvard the year following.

Ezra Ripley's son Samuel, Ralph's half-uncle, was also visiting at the Manse, having come from Waltham, where he was master of a school that was to see considerable success. He was also a minister, a kind-hearted, solid and intelligent man, and as Emerson said long after, at his uncle's death, no better kinsman ever lived. Young at this time, and newly married to a girl of great charm and notable culture, who was also spending a few days with the Ripleys, Samuel took an interest in his young nephew, whom he had seen only fleetingly until now. One afternoon as the two walked through the village together Samuel, who had noticed that the grown folk they met always had a word of greeting or affection for Ralph, while such boys as they encountered were more likely to shout a jeer at him or tweak his hat off or jostle him roughly in passing, came out bluntly in New England fashion:

"What's the reason, Ralph, that while the older people seem to like you, even to admire you, the boys dislike and try to pick a quarrel with you?"

Ralph, taken aback, had nothing to say. He hadn't felt that the boys disliked him; they were merely not interested in him, nor he, to be just, in them. As intimates, his own brothers sufficed. There was strong affection and sympathy between all four, and an understanding none among them found elsewhere. Not but that they each had friends; in Latin school two boys, Loring and Furness, both of whom would be distinguished in later life, were good friends of Ralph, a feeling that would last with their lives. Probably it came down to the fact that he was not interested in games and never joined in the school sports. His only backslidings were occasional truancies from school, when he would go off on solitary wanderings, a book under his arm – one of the novels he was not supposed to waste time over. He was in fact a good boy, a serenely unruffled boy, undisturbed by any attempts at teasing; above all, he was not cast in the regular pattern, that most unforgivable of sins with schoolboys. And even in a New England school he was described as undemonstrative, which meant something of a record. His type of quiet, observant humor had no point of contact with the slapstick jokes and noisy amusements of his fellows, while his unconsciously reserved, even proud, bearing irritated them.

Commenting on this condition in his maturity, Emerson

remarked that it was an odd fact that time had reversed matters; that while, as a boy, it was the old people who liked and admired him and the young ones who had no use for him, now that he was old it was youth that flocked to him with trust and affection, and his contemporaries or elders who disliked and distrusted him.

When Uncle Samuel, who was really troubled by this unpopularity of his nephew, mentioned his perplexity to Dr. Ripley, the old man snorted:

"Nonsense! The boy's all right. What if he doesn't wish to consort with a pack of young hoodlums? Is there anything wrong in that? They are going to grow up to be merchants and farmers, he's to be a minister. You're one yourself, Sam, and I don't know that playing rounders ever helped to make you one."

"I like to see a boy be a boy," Samuel answered. "But possibly he'll make more friends with those of his own age at Harvard next year. There seems to be no doubt but that he'll be ready then."

"He'll be ready. It's the question of money that isn't so certain. But I intend to pray the Lord on his behalf, and feel that a way will be found."

The Reverend Ezra had had proofs before this that prayer was answered. Only that very summer, marking the swift rise of a thunderstorm as he was getting in the last of his hay, he had laid his pitchfork aside while he called upon the Lord to remember it was his faithful servant whose crop was being threatened, and to beg that the storm might be diverted from the Ripley acres. The matter was attended to, and the hay garnered without so much as a drop falling upon it.

Whether because of his step-grandfather's intercession, or because Mr. Gould of the Latin school was a friend of John Thornton Kirkland, President of Harvard, and was able to have

Ralph appointed President's freshman, which meant that the boy would live and board at Wadsworth House, certain it is that Ralph was able to matriculate next year at the college. He was further helped by being made tutor over the President's young nephew, who would also be of the household, and this gave him a little ready money. Another source of income was provided by a grant of ten pounds yearly from a bequest managed by his father's old church. For the first year at least his needs were taken care of, and he passed his examination satisfactorily, "and was admitted without admonishment to study, as was the case with many," as Ruth proudly wrote Aunt Mary. William was already a senior, working his way through by teaching school during college vacations, and even part of the time while college held. Edward and Charles were doing well in their schools. The boys, born to be educated, were fulfilling their destiny.

Chapter IV

How drearily in College Halls
The Doctor stretched the hours;—
But in each pause we heard the calls
Of robins out of doors...

It was not the brains but the deportment of its students that most interested Harvard at the time when Ralph Waldo Emerson entered it. Every undergraduate act was governed by a vast number of fusty rules whose infraction was punished by fines and demerits, the demerits scoring against the boys' scholarship record. The result of this condition was that a boy was judged not by his mental ability but by his behavior, and often a dull lad who kept the rules stood higher in class than his mate who had brains but was less amenable to control. Harvard in 1817 was really little more than an advanced school for boys, and boys from thirteen and fourteen to seventeen and eighteen made up the student body. The curriculum was cut and dried; there was no elective system; the professors were uninspired men teaching by rote, who "drearily stretched the hours" with the sole ambition of stuffing the prescribed number of facts into the heads of their classes.

Fortunately, during young Emerson's undergraduate life, the stale air of the college halls would be stirred by a fresh, awakening breath. Three men in particular were responsible for the change. These were George Ticknor, professor of Romance Languages and Belles Lettres; Edward Tyrrel Channing, teaching English, brother of the great William Ellery Channing, who put an end to Calvinism in New England; Edward Everett, the first to occupy the Chair of Greek Literature. Of these three, Ticknor came to Harvard in 1819 and Everett the year following, so that only the last half of Ralph Waldo's college career was affected by these two men.

Both were fresh from years of study in Europe, study undertaken for the express purpose of filling their duties in the newly created courses, for Ticknor too was the first to fill his Chair. Later Longfellow followed him, Longfellow who, though but a year younger than Emerson, was four years later in matriculating for Bowdoin, from which college he was graduated in 1825.

Ticknor was a delightful man with a vigorous mind and a great enthusiasm for his subjects. He had been admitted to the bar, and was one of the few teachers at Harvard not a clergyman. This probably helped in making him far more interested in his students' brains than in their morals. Channing had an even greater personal charm and an equal freedom from the schoolmaster attitude; for young Emerson, moreover, he possessed a glamor, shed upon him by that brother of his. Ralph and his younger brother Edward had fallen under William Ellery's spell almost as soon as he began to preach in Boston, following him from one church to another in an ecstasy of admiration. Channing had been the first, in 1815, to come to the open defence of the Unitarians; but it was the man's eloquence, his tremendous spiritual devotion, which most moved the two brothers. Slight, his thin face dominated by a pair of eyes of singular size and brilliance, with a voice as clear and sweet as a bell, Channing bewitched his hearers, swept them along in the passionate stream of his thought, where for the first time in a Boston pulpit championship of beauty, art and spiritual freedom found stirring expression. Surely in listening to him

Ralph caught the first inspiration for the convictions which would rule his own belief; began to feel that "presence of God in mankind" which Channing was the first to preach.

As for Edward Everett, from that "new morning" when first the boy heard him lecture on the occasion of his introduction to the college, Ralph preferred the professor of Greek above all others. He became obsessed with him, never missing one of his lectures; speaking of him so much that he laughed, telling a friend that he couldn't touch on any subject but somehow it would swing to Everett. He wrote about him in the diary he kept, for he had the journal habit that was so much a characteristic of his times. "Germany," he commented, "had created criticism in vain for us until 1820, when E. E. returned from his five years in Europe and brought to Cambridge his rich results, which no one was so fitted by natural grace and the splendor of his rhetoric to introduce and recommend."

Ralph entered Harvard intending to make a record, if hard work could do this. He wrote to Edward on October 1, a day or two before entering, these resolved words:

"*My college life begins,* Deo volente, *and I hope and trust will begin with determined and ardent pursuit of real knowledge that will raise me high in the class while in college, and qualify me well for stations of future usefulness.*"

It was not long however before the colorless routine of the classes, the emphasis placed on mathematics—over which, as he wrote his indignant Aunt Mary, he was a "hopeless dunce"—and on the writings of Paley, Locke, Stewart and other dry-as-dusts, began desperately to bore him. Here was no bread for the spirit within him. His standing in class was mediocre; he plodded, showing never a feather of bright wings, whose soaring had been expected by his ex-master Gould, by President

Kirkland, by Aunt Mary. She wrote him furious letters, and his teachers shook their heads. Not that he failed to do what was necessary; simply that he did no more.

But the young Emerson was finding what he needed. In the college library were riches he had never been able to reach till now. He read Chaucer, Shakespeare, Plutarch, Montaigne, Plato; revelled in the English poets, particularly Moore and Byron. He loved Ben Jonson for his "vigorous phrases." He studied the English language with ardor, filling pages of his journals with striking words and phrases; and with one of his favorite books under his arm wandered in the green, still charm of Mount Auburn amid the ordered graves, deep in dreams or stirred by longings to be himself a poet. Not that he relinquished the plan of becoming a minister. That was a settled matter to which he alludes from time to time, sometimes oddly enough as "a peculiar pursuit at the distance of the years," sometimes definitely, as when he writes to William who was teaching school in Kennebunk, Maine, during the college vacation, that "*It appears to me the happiest earthly moment my most sanguine hopes can picture ... to have a home comfortable and pleasant to offer mother; in some feeble way to repay her for the cares and woes and inconveniences she has so often been subject to on our account alone ... when I am out of college I will,* Deo volente (he liked that expression) *study divinity and keep school at the same time — try to be a minister and to have a house.*"

One sees him, during his college years, quiet, reserved, friendly, yet making no intimate friend, mingling only slightly in the undergraduate life. In his freshman year running the errands of Dr. Kirkland, carrying the President's notes and messages to the students, in particular delivering the eagerly awaited announcements concerning the college exhibitions. To receive these the whole student body collected on the porch of University Hall, watching for the thin, narrow-chested figure of young Emerson, tall for his years, to come staidly out of the front door of Wadsworth House, the cards in his hands. Smiling composedly, completely impartial, appearing unaffected either by the delight of the winners or the disappointment of the losers, he delivered the announcements and quietly returned, his head a little bent, his step long and easy.

His sophomore year was marked by a row between that class and the college authorities that resulted in the withdrawal of the entire class as a protest against the expelling of several of its members. The trouble had its origin in a battle one night at Commons between the freshmen and the sophomores in which not only heads but practically all the supper dishes were broken. Emerson had not taken part in the fight, but he acted with his class, returning home until matters were arranged. The return of the class was celebrated by the founding of the Conventicle Club, a light-hearted, informal organization which ended with the end of the senior year. Its members met to smoke, tell stories, drink toasts in cheap wine. It was Ralph's only contact with the more sporting, convivial side of college life, and he enjoyed it, though he complained that drinking wine, instead of enlivening him, only made him "quieter and graver." But he wrote a long verse celebrating the sophomore defiance, calling it the *Rebelliad*, which he declaimed to considerable applause at one of the meetings.

More suited to his tastes was the Pythologian, founded by a classmate, Edward Kent, later to be Governor of Maine. This was an association of a number of young men interested in serious reading, holding weekly meetings for debate and other literary exercises. Two or three of the members were well-to-do, and these subscribed for several of the English reviews and the newly founded North American Review. At the close of the meetings a simple supper was served whose cost for the entire company never exceeded a couple of dollars.

To help defray the expenses of his second year Ralph waited on the junior class at table, and during vacations taught in his Uncle Samuel Ripley's school at Waltham. He roomed at number five, Hollis, with a student whose name was Dorr, a pleasant youth between whom and himself there was an amicable but only slight acquaintance.

The last two years of Ralph's college life were more interesting, because of Ticknor and Everett, and they were more comfortable. Besides the grant from the First Church he received a sum allotted to him from the Saltonstone Foundation which, with the earnings coming to him for his school-teaching, made it unnecessary to work his way. In addition he won, in junior year, the Boylston prize of thirty dollars for his dissertation on the character of Socrates, sending the sum immediately to his mother, begging her to purchase a fine shawl with it – alas, poor careful lady, she used it to pay off household bills! In senior year he won the Bowdoin prize for a paper on *The Present State of Ethical Philosophy*; both subjects curiously mature for his years.

For the rest, he went his uneventful way, finding always more value in his private reading than in college work. With his junior year the long series of journals, which continued with hardly a break until shortly before his death, began to reflect his thoughts; to hold comments, not at first on people, but on his reading and on moral principles, especially those exemplified in the classics. He would also enter lists of words, especially noting a new use, such as making an adjective of *signal*, or a verb of *register*, practices then unfamiliar. He confesses, too, to being fascinated by "chivalric story and fairyland bard," and asserts that above all he would like to sit in a library "which human pride and literary rivalship have made costly, splendid and magnificent," there to turn the pages of ponderous tomes on magic. His imagination was stirred, his heart lifted by the great poets and mighty thinkers of the past, brought to vivid life by Everett, pacing before the class on a platform behind which hung the new panorama of Athens lately presented to Harvard, while he poured out his learning, his enthusiasm, his own recollections in a torrent of gorgeous phrases.

During these two years young Emerson experienced an odd, unreal friendship for a freshman named Martin Gay, but known to his own classmates as "Cool" Gay. This boy was about the same age as Ralph, but of an entirely different temperament, his whole being bent toward the sciences and particularly medicine. Nevertheless, he fascinated the senior student, and Ralph used to follow him about, staring at him fixedly, yet always dodging any real meeting. Indeed, he spoke to him only a few times during the two years, but he admits in his journal that he found himself "wholly wrapped up in conjectures of his thought and character." What Gay thought of the distant yet marked attention of the silent upper-classman we shall never know; he certainly made no effort to develop it into any personal contact. The two would dodge each other on the college walks, dive into a convenient doorway or dash down an alley to escape meeting face to face; and then Emerson would go to his room and set down his bewilderment, blaming now himself, now Gay. The probable fact is that the lonely young man, fascinated by something in the freshman, built up from this charm and his fancy an ideal friend, the friend whom he wanted. He sketches this friend, who shall be different from any individual he has yet seen, a man "with a solemn cast of thought, full of poetic feeling, an idolater of friendship and possessing a vein of rich, sober thought." Gay was none of these things, but a clever, lively youngster who entered heartily into Harvard's social life without neglecting his studies, spurred by a clear-eyed ambition that in time made him one of New England's noted doctors.

Far more satisfactory as a companion was Edward, who came to Harvard as a freshman in Ralph's senior year. The two brothers shared room number nine at Hollis, happy to be together. Affection ran deep between the Emerson boys, none of whom seem to have had a close friend among men as compared with the intimate ties binding them to each other. This was especially true of the three younger brothers. William had no touch of the genius that burned in them, lacked the imagination, the creative force that was theirs. As Ralph wrote of him, he was "early old;" a staid schoolmaster at seventeen, head of his own successful school at eighteen; taking the place of head of the family, turning in his earnings to help his mother and his brothers, doing his duty with a simple devotion that took itself for granted. He had the trust and the love of that family as well as their admiration, but was rather more the counsellor than the companion.

In August 1821, Ralph Waldo Emerson graduated, number twenty-nine in a class of fifty-nine, his standing just bringing him into the rank of those who took part in the commencement exercises. He was also the class poet, though this honor only came to him after six others in the class had refused it. In the exercises he was given the part of John Knox, in a Colloquy on Knox, William Penn and John Wesley. He was utterly uninterested, with the result that he did not properly memorize his part, and had to be loudly prompted while he hesitated and stammered on his way, thankful when the ordeal was over. He left the college without a regret. It probably did little in developing the genius that was in him. Coming back on a visit to the place the following February, he says as much in his journal:

"I have not much cause, I sometimes think, to wish my Alma Mater well, personally; I was not often highly flattered by success, and was every day mortified by my own ill fate, or ill conduct. Still, when I went today to the ground where I had had the brightest thoughts of my little life, and filled up the little measure of my knowledge, and had felt sentimental for a time, and poetical for a time, and had seen many fine faces, and traversed many fine walks, and enjoyed much pleasant, friendly or learned society,—I felt a crowd of pleasant thoughts as I went posting from place to place and room to chapel."

This was all the young man could find to say for his four years at his Alma Mater. Like Hawthorne at Bowdoin he had been undistinguished as an undergraduate. College did little for and meant little to either of these men of genius, different as they were in temperament, expression, and understanding of life. From Bowdoin Hawthorne went into those five years of seclusion and solitary literary labor in the family home at Salem that form so strange an interlude in his existence, while Emerson took up school-teaching, a task he hated, a task that appeared to him a bitter waste of time. He was perhaps as close to despair during the next two years as he ever got, not because his lot was hard, for in many ways he was more comfortable and the family as a whole was certainly better off than it had been since the father's death, but because of the burden of self-distrust that weighed his spirit down; because he was "drearily stretching the hours" for his students, as once they had been stretched for him. After a year's work he describes himself and his situation in these almost desperate phrases:

"*I am a changed person in condition, in hope.. I was then* (at graduation) *delighted with my recent honors; traversing my chamber flushed and proud of a poet's fancies and the day when they were to be exhibited; pleased with ambitious prospects, and careless because ignorant of the future. But now I am a hopeless schoolmaster, just entering upon years of trade to which no distinct limit is placed; toiling through this miserable employment without even the poor satisfaction of discharging it well; for the good suspect me and the geese dislike me. Hope, it is true, still hangs out, though at farther distance, her gay banners; but I have found her cheat once, twice, many times, and shall I trust the deceiver again? . . . Good people will tell me that it is a Judgment and lesson for my character, to make me fitter for the whereto I aspire; but if I come out a dispirited, mature, broken-hearted miscreant,—how will man or myself be bettered? . . . In twelve days I shall be nineteen years old; which I count a miserable thing. Has any other educated person lived so many years and lost so many days?"*

He goes on to describe himself as lazy, as envious of the success of his fellows, as without energy to mount the trail he wants to follow, and concludes:

"I have not the kind affections of a pigeon. Ungenerous and selfish, cautious and cold, I . . . have not sufficient feeling to speak a natural, hearty welcome . . . there is not . . . one being to whom I am attached with warm and entire devotion . . . not one whose interests I have nearly and dearly at heart; and this I say at the most susceptible age of man . . . a true picture of a barren and desolate soul."

It was once the fashion to regard youth as the season of light-hearted joy, and to let it go at that. Now we know better, know that youth has more than its share of griefs and despairs. There was a vast spirit in young Emerson and a great longing to find fit expression. Nineteen! At the beginning of everything, yet fancying himself already at the end. Day after day carrying on the routine of his brother's school for young ladies, established in the Boston house; shy, flushing at sly glances and small snickers; aware that he was giving none of the best of himself; unaware that he was doing more than was expected and doing it well. He wanted to lead the way to the immortal heights where the great philosophers and poets debated transcendental themes; to seek the measure of man's soul; to put into unforgettable words the deep thought within him; not to potter over little dates and dead facts, correct errors in grammar, keep his class in order. A hopeless schoolmaster! He felt that he was caught, trapped; that this was to be his future as well as his present, for it is part of youth's burden to think the present eternity, and not the fluid, vanishing thing it is.

A distant cousin, George Barrell Emerson, of Maine, was boarding with Mrs. Emerson while he taught at the Classical School in Boston. He gives a very different picture of the same period. Edward, a shining light at Harvard, where he took every prize and dominated his class, was also teaching during vacations and with success. William's school was making money, the property left Ruth by her father bringing in a small income, the household busy and apparently content. "William," wrote George, "has the sweetest voice I ever listened to. Ralph is admirable. Edward Bliss the most modest and genial, the most beautiful and graceful speaker, a universal favorite. Charles Chauncey bright and ready, full of sense, ambitious of distinction and capable of it." And as for Ralph's ability as a teacher, William thought so highly of it that he decided to leave the school to his brother, while he went himself to Germany, there to prepare for the ministry. He had enough money in hand to take him abroad and keep him there for a while, when more could be sent him. He smiled at Ralph's terror over the prospect of being left to manage everything; told him he was practically doing just this already.

"In another year or two you can save enough money to pay your way through Divinity School, or to join me abroad. You are an excellent teacher, the girls like you, you have a dignity beyond your years. All you want," and he smiled, "is more self-assurance, and I have found that comes with practice."

It was spring, with all the lovely urge and delicate bloom of that season in New England. Before sailing William wanted to take a fortnight's vacation, and he wanted Ralph with him. The two set forth together on a long tramp that took them to Northborough, where they stayed in a pretty farmhouse, wandered in the woods, talked over the future. It was a pleasant time for the two, and heartened by his brother's praise, by the confidence he showed him, Ralph, after William's departure, settled down to make a good job of his schooling, though he continued to detest it.

CHAPTER V

The Consecration and the Poet's Dream

RALPH WALDO continued to teach his school until the end of the year 1824 with success if not with pleasure. Some months after William's departure Ruth had moved from the house in Boston to a cottage on the farm of a Mr. Stedman, in Canterbury, a lovely region of hilly ground through which ran a brook. Pines grew there, shedding their tangy fragrance from whispering needles, and the country peace was seldom broken by even casual traffic through the shadowy lane passing farm and cottage. Long since Boston has spread past Canterbury, but a part of the green loveliness is perpetuated in what is now called Franklin Park. When the Emersons lived there, however, the city lay four miles away, miles tramped each morning and evening by Ralph, going back and forth to his school, the schoolroom having been retained when the house was given up. During those walks, and under the pines in warm spring and sultry summer days he dropped the school from his mind and plunged into long ponderings on the nature of man, on religion and dogma; he read the poets, he wrote down in his journal verses of his own. He had sent his Aunt Mary these journals, at her request. She may have been taken aback at their gloominess, but if so she did not let him know it. She wrote, returning them, that she preferred their tone to one of smug complacency, said that she found his sense of failure far more hopeful for his spiritual good than any rapid rise to success could have given him. What she dreaded for him was "the moment when your Muse shall be dragged into éclat. Then will your guardian angel tremble."

Ralph smiled at that. He thought the angel had little cause as yet for anxiety.

During the vacations he took from teaching he indulged a growing love for long hikes, tramping often as many as twenty or more miles in a day. Sometimes he spent the night at the house of a friend or a relative, sometimes at an inn. His natural if shy friendliness led him to talk with any stranger encountered on the way and he liked nothing more than to listen to the conversation of farmers and mechanics, the village blacksmith, the host of the inn. All his life he liked that stout and shrewd New England breed, men who made their living from the earth and from the crafts. He was not so well pleased on these walks with the sermons to which he listened on Sundays. Mere rehashing of stale dogmas, he thought, with nothing to lift up the heart in all their dreary length. As he sat in his pew he began to imagine himself in the preacher's place, and to feel that when he stood in a pulpit it was with a different spirit and in different words that he would speak of God to man. These grim clergymen seemed bent on separating the two, in cleaving between man and his God an impassable gulf; but was it not the pastor's duty to bring them closer, to unite them? He so believed.

Most of the time at Canterbury his mother and he were alone. Edward, after graduating with the highest honors in 1824, had gone to Roxbury and set up a school of his own which flourished. There was something wonderful about Edward, a shining warmth, a natural eloquence, a mind that seized without seeming effort the very heart of what was offered and yet forgot no detail. He was reading for the law as well as teaching his school, snatching only a few days of relaxation from work, coming on hardly more than momentary visits to his mother. When he came he and Ralph would lie together under the pines, in eager talk; or spend half the night turning over books, commenting on the new literary school in England, on French political ideas, renewing familiar contact with the classics. Edward intended to be a statesman as well as a lawyer; hoped perhaps to emulate in the days to come the greatness of a Daniel Webster, who was beginning to grow gigantic in men's eyes.

"We are on the threshold of great things, Ralph. What may not the future hold for our generation? We are learning to break the rusty chains that have fettered our fathers, and no hope, no success is too daring, too impossible for us. In Europe great changes are becoming commonplaces, and they are stirring here. It is a grand time in which to be young, with the years waiting for us. William and you, Charles and I, you two in the church, we two in the law, what cannot we accomplish?"

"Meanwhile," Ralph retorted, with a kind of amused glumness, "we teach a few boys and girls who sit yawning at their desks and wish we were a hundred miles away."

Edward laughed. At least the teaching was bringing in money, money that would put Ralph through Divinity School and allow himself to study in Europe.

But Ruth was troubled by Edward's frailness, by the shadow of fatigue under his too-brilliant eyes. She begged him not to work so continuously, wished he would eat more. "You're thinner every time I see you," she told him.

"All the Emersons are thin," he answered her, smiling into her dark, uplifted eyes. "Work doesn't tire me; I delight in it. But I promise not to burn the midnight oil too often."

It was decided that with the start of the new year Ralph should begin to study at the Harvard Divinity School. He would be accepted in the middle class and with hard work might be ready to be ordained in a year. Ruth would go to Concord to stay at the Old Manse for the present, for her son had taken a room in the school. It was a ground-floor room, in the northeast corner of the building; a cold, cheerless room, but it was cheap. Economy was necessary, and a little cold, a little damp did not matter. It was not in the Emerson character to balk at hardships.

Summing up the three and a half years since his graduation Ralph set down the result in his journal. He had earned nearly three thousand dollars, paid whatever debts he had, and there was money enough in the bank to take care of him during the beginning of his studies. He could earn more at teaching before this was used up. In addition there were several persons "obligated." And he had written at least two or three hundred pages which, he declared, "will be of use to me." The Boston property belonging to Ruth was bringing in about two hundred dollars a year, with the probability that it would do better in the future.

William was still in Germany, living at Göttingen, with Goethe for an honored friend. He had decided finally to give up the ministry and was studying law. "Come and join me," he wrote. "I can help you, and you will be delighted with this place." But Ralph did not believe it wise to spend as much money as would be required for the voyage; nor, he thought, was it necessary. No time would be lost at the Harvard school, and he wanted to begin his life work without further procrastination.

During the summer at Canterbury he wrote various friends as well as his scattered family that he was going to drop the name of Ralph in favor of Waldo. The family name of Waldo was beloved, and he preferred it to his given name. He continued to use Ralph in a professional or business way with the rest of his signature, but from this time on he was always called Waldo by his intimates and so wrote to them.

The new year, 1825, therefore found him installed in his northeast chamber, attending on the school and plunging with fervor into the work required. But alas, as Burns had sung some fifty years earlier, the plans of mice and men gang aft agley! A month passed when suddenly young Emerson's health began to break. Not only did he suffer acute pains over most of his body, but his eyes were so badly affected that he was forbidden to continue his reading. There was no use staying on in the school, and after a brief period with his mother at the Old Manse, Waldo recovered enough to accept the invitation of an uncle living on a farm near Newton. He spent the spring and summer helping with the farm work, not too strenuously, gradually regaining strength and health. The outdoor life, the good farm food, as well as the relaxation from brain work all lent their aid. He enjoyed the life, the talks with fellow laborers, especially one stout old Methodist who upheld the power of prayer so strenuously, with so passionate a conviction, that Waldo was impressed. It interested him to encounter so deep a faith, such simple trust. He liked this old man, a good worker, a firm believer; and though he might not subscribe to all his new friend's convictions, he was moved by what was strong and beautiful in them. He set down the man's arguments, and later on, preaching his first sermon, used prayer as his theme.

By September he felt well enough to teach in a near-by public school, and before that tutored two lads preparing for the college examinations, an easy job. His health continued to improve and he had almost decided upon returning to the Divinity School when Edward took his turn at being ill. By January he was so bad that it was decided to send him to the Mediterranean on a long sea cruise, and Waldo took over the rest of the term at the Roxbury school, which was to close at the end of March.

It was a time of stress and anxiety. Edward ill; Waldo still at times suffering from rheumatic pains; Charles, after a magnificent record at Harvard, trying to find school work that would allow him, also, to study law. With April Ruth decided to make a home in Cambridge, where Waldo could be properly taken care of, go on with his reading and teach a small school that could meet in the house. In September Edward came home, his health apparently entirely restored. When the good news of his coming reached his brother, Waldo entered these happy words in his journal:

"*Hark, I can hear on the eastern wind almost the harp of my coming Orpheus! He sets his sail and flies over the grim flood. Breathe soft the winds, and shine softly on him the autumnal sun; speed his bark, for his heart is noble and his hand is strong, and the good of others is given into his hand.*"

He came, a radiant vision of young manhood, welcomed with joy. At once he set to work, for he had gone into debt to pay for the trip, but he promised greater caution for the future. A promise he did not keep, for there was in him a burning restless energy, a vaulting ambition he could not control. Though, agreeable to his mother's wishes, he did not attempt to reëstablish his school; instead taking youths for tutoring and acting as confidential agent for several firms in conjunction with his law reading. He succeeded so well both at the tutoring and as agent that gradually more and more of what should have been his leisure was devoted to such work. Once his debts were repaid, he promised himself a long vacation, but meanwhile . . .

Waldo's Cambridge school for boys prospered. The students liked him and he preferred teaching boys to teaching girls. What impressed the school most was their teacher's strong moral nature, his horror of anything approaching coarseness, together with the real interest he took in them individually, outside of their class work. He was always ready to talk over future plans with any one of the boys, to suggest this or that book or author, to discuss with him his future prospects. One of these boys was Richard Henry Dana, then eleven years old, who was not only to become one of New England's most distinguished lawyers, but to reach international and enduring fame by way of a little book called *Two Years Before the Mast.* This volume was published in 1840, finding almost instant popularity. Waldo recognized its excellence with delight, writing to William this bit of praise: "Have you seen young Dana's book? As good as Robinson Crusoe, and all true. He was my scholar once, but he never learned this of me, more's the pity." Perhaps not. Yet Emerson's exquisite appreciation for the English language, for style in writing and clarity of vision may have contributed more than he guessed to young Dana's equipment. Emerson never gave himself the credit he deserved as a teacher, subconsciously aware that he had so much more to give than could find its way through routine channels.

Owing to the irregularity with which he had to pursue his theological studies Waldo was not graduated from the Divinity School, but he was, in October of that year, 1826, "approbated" to preach by the Middlesex Association of Ministers. He thereupon closed his school for good, the last he was ever to teach, and preached his first sermon at his uncle Samuel Ripley's church in Waltham, the sermon with prayer for its theme which his Methodist fellow laborer had inspired. He produced a favorable impression. His voice was beautiful, his words well-chosen, moving and direct. His bearing, at once kind and aloof, his tall slenderness in the black ministerial robes, the finely modeled, sensitive face, won his congregation immediately. Uncle Samuel was greatly pleased. This young man would decidedly do. The family could be proud of him.

He had passed his twenty-third year in May. Life so far had held for him far more of intellectual than emotional development. He had thought profoundly on those moral problems with which his age was contending. He had read enormously, and he had read the best of classical, medieval and contemporary literature. His family affections were deep, if undemonstrative, but beyond these he had made no intimate contacts with any human being. He was lonely; he had felt unhappiness, the unhappiness of youth that feels itself unused, unplumbed, which, longing to give, finds no one to take the gift. Now he had attained the aim toward which, from babyhood, he had been set. He was a preacher, dedicated to the service of his fellowmen with all he was and all he knew. This service must bring him closer to humanity, to human beings in their separate entities. He would preach to his people, he would stand beside the dying, he would join young lovers in holy matrimony.

Until he was called to a church of his own he would fill in for brother clergymen, as was the custom. It was excellent practice and he looked forward to it with interest. But now again illness interposed. The Emerson brothers, born to be educated, were paying the price exacted for the unremitting devotion to their birthright and the denials and hardships it had involved. A week after his first sermon Waldo developed a cough, a touch of fever. By November he was really ill, so ill that the doctor called in thought the New England winter might be too much for him.

"Get him south until spring comes," he told the perturbed family, and Waldo was content to go. "A little mouse is gnawing in my bosom," he confided to his journal. That little mouse was a busy one in New England, and its gnawing was usually followed by what was then called consumption, the white plague that filled so many graves in New England with the bodies of youths and maidens, which few families entirely escaped.

Uncle Samuel, that kinsman who was never to fail in a pinch, came forward with offers to pay expenses. On the 25th, therefore, the young man sailed on a small coastwise vessel, spending twelve storm-tossed, miserable days in the uncomfortable quarters assigned him. The ship took him as far as Charleston, where he stayed until early in January; but the weather was bitter cold, with rain and sleet. His health was not being improved, so, this time aboard a small sloop, Waldo continued his journey southward as far as St. Augustine, Florida.

It would have been hard to find a greater contrast to Boston. The population was chiefly Spanish and negro, one as lazy and shiftless as the other. The Spaniards ran gambling halls, danced, fiddled, held masques and fêtes, sang all night and slept most of the day. The negroes, who were all slaves, dug clams and caught fish for their masters, tended what small gardens there were, cooked and occasionally cleaned. The few Americans were all officeholders or traders. The Catholic priest spent most of his time in prison for debt, being let out to attend to his churchly duties or to attend a masque, where his lively if coarse wit was appreciated, and his skill in imitating the drunken sailor whose costume he wore delighted the party. Even the American Bible Society held its services in a room of Government House that opened on the court where the slave market was held, unfortunately on Sundays at the same hour as that of Divine worship. So that, as Emerson wrote home, "one ear listens to the tidings of great joy, the other to 'going, going, gone,'" and added that, without changing your seat, "you could arrange to send the Scriptures to Africa, or bid on 'four children without a mother,' who had been kidnapped from that country."

But this southern sojourn taught the New Englander a needed lesson, not to work too hard. The Emerson curse, as he wrote to William, still in Germany, was to overdo. He knew now that they must learn to rest, to idle, to be with "laughing, cheerful people" at least part of the time. That way, and only that way, lay health.

Seating herself at the spinet she played her own accompaniments, and Waldo thought her voice the loveliest he had ever heard

He preached once or twice in St. Augustine, and on his slow progress north both in Charleston, where he spent most of April, and in Alexandria, near Washington, where he remained for May, using sermons he had composed during his sessions at the Divinity School. He found that preaching brought back that gnawing pain in the chest, and wrote Aunt Mary that perhaps this would ride him till his death. In June he was back home, visiting at the Old Manse where Ruth was again staying, then returning to that north room at Divinity Hall to continue his studies and to preach in different pulpits as occasion offered.

In those days a minister was expected to preach all day long, an interminable morning service being followed by another almost as lengthy in the afternoon. Waldo's strength proved unequal to such a strain. He gave up afternoon work therefore, going to listen to other men instead. Less and less did what he heard seem to him worth listening to. Mere mouthings of outworn creeds, stale clichés, tiresome reiterations. Nothing fresh or strong or pure to bring men's hearts, rejoicing, to their God. No one dared to think for himself.

One of his visiting assignments took him to Concord, then known as New Concord, New Hampshire, to preach in the recently dedicated Unitarian Church there. He greatly pleased the congregation, meeting them afterwards in the lobby or porch to receive their friendly congratulations. One among them, Colonel W. A. Kent, took him home to dine. At the house Waldo met the Colonel's stepdaughter, Ellen Louise Tucker, who had not been well enough to attend the service. She was a lovely young thing of seventeen, looking more angel than woman, young Emerson thought. Modest, frail as a windflower, yet with a clear, true intelligence that revealed itself when she spoke, which was not often. It was obvious that the Colonel adored her. After the meal was over Ellen was asked to sing by her stepfather, consenting with the grace, the simplicity that showed in all her acts and words. Seating herself at the spinet she played her own accompaniments, and Waldo thought her voice the loveliest he had ever heard. It was small, but true, clear and of a haunting sweetness. He tried to tell her how he admired it, but became confused, stammered, fell silent. Her eyes lifted to his in a sudden troubled wonder . . .

The young minister was to sleep at the house of another member of the congregation, and presently made his farewells. He left next morning without seeing Ellen again.

He could not, however, forget her. In the gloomy room at Divinity Hall she seemed to be a presence, a remembered loveliness. The tinkle of the spinet, the lifting notes of a delicate voice mingled with the scratch of his pen. He found himself leaning back in his chair, dreaming. The poet in him stirred, and he wanted to write verses whose subject should be Ellen. Ellen! How beautiful the name.

He was suddenly frightened. This would not do. He made up his mind not to return to Concord, cancelled the return visit he had promised.

CHAPTER VI

O, hasten! 'tis our time
Ere yet the red summer
Scorch our delicate prime . . .

IN THE spring of 1828 a terrific blow fell. Edward suffered a nervous collapse so severe that Waldo, hastily summoned by affrighted friends, decided to take his brother to Concord where, at the Old Manse, he could be watched over, and where the quiet loveliness of the country springtime would help him to recovery. At first he seemed better, then a series of fainting spells alarmed everybody. Ruth, who had come to nurse him, feared for his life with each attack. Between the periods of unconsciousness he muttered in delirium, and as he recovered bodily strength, this madness increased. By the end of June there was no possibility of doubt; Edward, the most brilliant, the most fascinating of the brothers, was violently insane. Waldo wrote to William a letter expressing the agony of the family. There he lay, "the admired, eloquent, striving boy, a maniac."

Waldo had taken him to the establishment of a physician for mental cases in Charlestown. Throughout the summer he remained in bed, the shell of his former self, recognizing no one at first, swept away into the confused, isolated world of insanity. William returned from Germany in haste, to be ready to do what he could. There was nothing better for him to do, however, than to accept the position which had been offered him in a leading firm of New York lawyers. The salary he was to receive would help defray expenses. After a visit to his suffering brother William took the coach back to that city, a long, tiresome journey. He had greatly matured during his long absence, was now a man of solid judgment, sound common sense, with an assured future. He had Ruth's own excellent health, her serenity of spirit. He had worked hard abroad but he had not overworked. The "curse of overdoing" had not fallen on him, Waldo was glad to note.

"The doctor tells me he believes Edward curable," William said, as the two brothers waited for the coach on which he was to depart. "You must see that he does not take up his labors too soon after recovery. You and I, Ralph, must be the drag anchors for our ambitious younger brothers. Charles is like Edward, brilliant above the common, headed for great things, but without our sense of measure. I've been talking to Charles, and this calamity has at least that much of good, it shows the boy that there's a limitation to human strength beyond which you must not go. But keep watch over him."

With the coming of October Edward showed great improvement, and by November the doctor pronounced him cured. He was feeble after his long confinement, must be built up, needed a bracing climate, but his mind was sound again. Waldo had finished at the Divinity School, but was not ready yet to seek a permanent church. An offer to help in the work of the church at New Concord decided him to go there with Edward. The dry fine winter among the New Hampshire hills was just what he needed, and Waldo would be earning something. It seemed providential.

There was Ellen, of course. But that was over, a thing of the past, and Waldo could smile at the boyish infatuation which had so disturbed him. A lovely young woman, certainly. He would be glad to see her again; to hear her sing, too. Edward, who delighted in music, would like her voice. It was a cheerful, charming household, just what his brother needed in his struggle back to normal health and spirits. Really, Waldo thought, as the stage took the two northward, and the bare, yellow, frost-bitten fields of Massachusetts gave way to snow, really, he had been foolish to be so alarmed.

Colonel Kent, friendly and hospitable, waited on the Emersons the day following their arrival. They must dine with him and his family. The minister Waldo was to help was coming; he and his new assistant would have much to talk over.

Waldo accepted with a sudden inward tumult. He explained that he was not a regular assistant, but would fill in when necessary. The present minister was serving another church for the time, while its pastor was away on a prolonged visit. He would himself have to devote a good deal of his time to Edward. It was very kind of the Colonel . . . he found himself stammering a little, felt himself blush . . .

But when, later that day, he and Ellen met again in the square, peaceful room of the Colonel's colonial house, where the fire in the Franklin stove burned cheerily and the sun shone in through icicle-trimmed windows, Waldo felt an upspring of joy in his heart. Why had he stayed away? What mattered beside looking at her, listening to her? How the little blue silk gown became her, with its snowy fichu held by a cameo brooch and the white undersleeves clasped about the slim wrists with tiny ruffles of lace. How little she was, how the parted fair hair bunched over her ears framed to perfection that delicate wind-flower face!

Would Miss Ellen sing for them, the young minister begged. He wanted his brother to hear her.

Ellen sang. There was a flush on her cheeks, her eyes were bright and happy. As the days passed she sang a good deal, sang as she tripped about her household tasks; or she fell suddenly quiet, her hands with her knitting lying relaxed in her lap, her eyes on the fire, dreaming. Her mother and sister smiled at each other. There were few days when young Mr. Emerson did not drop in, if but for a few moments, perhaps merely to borrow a book, or to ask the Colonel some question about the parish. Both brothers came to the Christmas dinner; Edward, who was mending fast, very fine in a new blue coat, but Waldo, or so Ellen thought, most distinguished in his ministerial black, with his high stock carefully folded.

In the spring, shortly before the two brothers, (Edward being by now quite recovered), were to leave for Boston, Waldo wrote to William, who was doing well in New York:

"*Dear Brother: I have the happiness to inform you that I have been now for one week engaged to Ellen Louise Tucker, a young lady who, if you will trust me, is the fairest and best of her kind . . . It is now a year since I became acquainted with Ellen . . . but I thought I had got over my blushes and my wishes when now I determined to go into that dangerous neighborhood on Edward's account. But the presumptuous man was overthrown (and) is now as happy as it is safe in life to be. She is seventeen years old, and very beautiful, by universal consent.*"

It was only a month after this happy consummation, however, that anxiety took the place of joy. Ellen fell ill. The distracted mother told Waldo, who hastened to New Concord at once, that the doctor feared consumption.

"She's always been delicate, as you know, but none of us ever dreamed—she wants to see you. She's in her own chamber, not in bed, but sitting in a reclining chair. You mustn't let her talk much, Mr. Emerson . . ."

He found her cheerful, in spite of her weakness. Of course she would soon be well again! They were all overanxious. He kissed the slender little hand, gazed at her with a desperate hopefulness that tried to look content and at ease.

"I'm far too happy to be really ill," the girl told him. "If this had happened before we loved each other, I do not know how badly I might have suffered. But you will see, I shall soon be up again . . ."

He left her, somewhat comforted. And truly, the news was presently better. Ellen was getting stronger, she was able to eat, she was coming downstairs again. Her betrothed lover came up as often as possible through the rest of the summer and fall. Once the extreme hot weather passed she gathered fresh strength and by the doctor's advice spent hours sitting in the sunny garden, reading or sewing.

Meanwhile Waldo continued to serve different churches, preaching in his step-grandfather's church in Concord and in other near-by villages and towns. In Boston he was heard several times, making a good impression. He read much, added to his journals. Edward was beginning to work at the law again; Charles was teaching school. By February Ellen's health was improving decidedly. The month before, Waldo had received a call to Boston's Second Church, popularly called Old North. Its minister, Dr. Ware, an old family friend, had accepted a chair in the Divinity School and must have an assistant in his church work. Would Mr. Emerson take the position?

Waldo had hesitated, not for his own sake, but for his "Beauty's." Could she endure safely the rigors of the Boston climate? In February the doctor felt secure in saying yes. Apparently the disease that had threatened was controlled. Waldo could see for himself, on his visits, that his love was coming back to health. Overjoyed, he wrote Dr. Ware that he would gladly accept the offered work, subject of course to the decision of the Committeemen. They proved to be overwhelmingly for him, giving him seventy-four of a possible seventy-nine votes. On March 11, 1829, he was ordained, and became Dr. Ware's assistant. The Doctor, however, had only waited to see how capable the young man would prove, and in April, entirely satisfied of his ability, he gave up the church to devote his own energies entirely to the Divinity School, and Waldo took complete charge.

The marriage between himself and his fair Ellen was planned for the autumn. He would have time to become fully accustomed to his duties and to make ready the new home. Ruth would live with the young pair, seeing to it that Ellen did not overwork. The boy's dream, of becoming a minister and of making a home where his mother should be safe and comfortable, was fulfilled, and how much more than fulfilled! No dream had ever adumbrated such happiness as was now promised him.

Expressing something of what he felt, he wrote to his Aunt Mary, drawing a contrast between the present moment and the past, with its hardships and troubles, the "straitened lines of poverty" through which he and his brothers "had walked up to manhood," saying:

"*I lean always to that ancient superstition (if it is such, though drawn from a wise survey of human affairs) which taught men to beware of unmixed prosperity, for nemesis keeps watch to overthrow the high. Well, now look at the altered prospect. William has begun to live by the law. Edward has recovered his reason and his health. Charles is prospering in all ways. Waldo is comparatively well and comparatively successful—far more so than his friends, out of the family, anticipated. Now I add to all this felicity a particular felicity which makes my own glass very much larger and fuller. And I straightway say, 'Can this hold?'*"

In his first sermon at his church Waldo had set forth, as was the custom, his own point of view regarding his convictions. He thought that preaching was being held in too narrow a range. Christianity, he told his congregation, was not a mere expounding from a text, but an infinite, universal law; the revelation of a Deity whose being the soul could not reject without denying itself. In drawing his illustrations he intended to draw on the common round of life, and he wished to remind carpers, if there were any, that "Our Lord condescended to explain Himself by allusions to every homely fact," and were He among men today would surely, in speaking, "make use of what lay near at hand, the printing press, the loom, the phenomena of steam, of gas."

His boyish admiration for high-sounding rhetoric had faded. He noted in his journal that he had no intention of "straining to say what is unutterable," of indulging in "vain belching with the imbecile use of great words."

As he promised, so he performed. His direct and simple sermons shocked some of the orthodox; but most, and in particular the younger members of his flock, were delighted. Already he began to turn from dogma; to declare that the importance of a sermon was not in its exposition of a creed, but in its power to draw men closer to God. And in his journal, he set down that "in the Bible you are not instructed to be a Unitarian, or a Calvinist, or an Episcopalian."

On the last day of September, in the parlor of the pleasant Kent house, he and Ellen were married; he being twenty-six and she eighteen. Their home was ready for them at Chardon Place, Boston, and Madam Emerson already installed. Ruth was the easiest, even as Aunt Mary was the most difficult, person with whom to live. She loved her daughter-in-law from the first, for Ellen was easy to love, and Ellen returned the affection. The three made a household at peace with itself.

For the first time in his life Waldo knew happiness, the happiness existent in an exquisite companionship completed by that magic which is first love, passionate and deep, filling him with radiance as a lamp is filled with light. He had been lonely until then, so lonely, so apart from any vital clutch on another human being that he had suffered a kind of panic, fearing himself too cold, too self-centered ever to break through the iron ring of isolation. His affection for his family he took as a matter of course; in a sense his brothers, his mother, were a part of himself. There was, moreover, practically no demonstration of feeling between them. Ruth was always cold in manner, reserved if gentle. Once, long ago, when he and one of his brothers had suddenly decided on a day-long tramp and had set out without informing their mother, they returned to find her beside herself with anxiety. "God be praised that you are safe," she had cried. "I have been in agony for you, my sons!" Ralph had been deeply moved by this plain evidence of her love, and years later he had written of that experience in his journal, saying that he "had gone to bed in an ecstasy of bliss."

But Ellen was not afraid to show her love, not afraid to be happy. Her warbling voice made a thread of music through the days. She had brought her spinet with her and there were few evenings when she did not sing to it, and she had a lovely way of singing at work that her husband adored.

Emerson was treading the path of his father before him, and was apparently established for life. He was appointed Chaplain of the Senate, opening the debates and proceedings of that body of stately gentlemen with prayer, pleasingly brief, under the beautiful dome of the state capitol, covered with copper that had been rolled by Paul Revere. He also took his place on the school board and gave invitation sermons at other Boston churches. It was he who preached what was called the "charity sermon" at his father's church, because the offering taken at this service was devoted to charity, and a minister certain to fill the building was always secured. In fact, the new minister's fame had got abroad; there were those who declared he was an angel, and that, after listening to his beautiful voice, even the singing of the choir sounded harsh.

On the other hand there were duties in which he was not so satisfactory. At funerals, people complained, he was not at his best; and at deathbeds the expected commonplaces did not fall easily from his lips. With the dying, as so often with the living, he appeared somewhat embarrassed, hesitant. It was impossible for him to respond to a conventional demand for grief, or for heartiness, with any ease. He did not like to invade other people's privacy, and withdrew into a somewhat chill reserve at any uninvited attempt to invade his own.

But with these exceptions he was successful as minister and more than successful as preacher. He was beginning to be a figure in Boston, a Boston to whom the name of Emerson meant much. Old folk compared him, and not unfavorably, with his father. There was an unexpectedness, something fresh and original in his preaching, and though it sometimes startled it certainly never bored. Ellen, flowerlike, gentle in manner, sweetly bearing herself as the minister's wife, was liked by all. "She's only a child," they said, "yet so wise, so full of sympathy."

The winter passed and all was well. But with March Ellen began to cough. It was a cruel March, with bitter east winds and violent changes in temperature, a true Boston March. Suddenly she was worse, so much worse that Waldo took alarm. She must be taken south, and with this her doctor, come down from New Concord for a consultation, agreed. She would shake it off in the sun and the mildness of a Baltimore or Washington spring.

Securing a colleague to take over his church work for him, Waldo himself took his wife away. Her sister went with them, for he could not stay long and wanted to be free to leave her to recover completely. Almost at once she made a decided recovery, and he was able to make his return with heartfelt relief. She was getting well, and once the warm weather was safely back, could come home to him.

The Chardon Place house seemed painfully empty when he came back, but the blessing of work was waiting. Waldo plunged into it with relief; finding always some moment in the day to write his Ellen, sending her poems as well as letters; telling her, in every way he knew, how wonderful she was to him, how dear and how needed. Relating details of his parish work, too, noting the themes of his sermons. As spring began to bloom again he sent her a poem describing the return of the flowers, saying that they looked for her and missed her and called to her to return, since spring could not be spring with her away.

In May she was home, seeming as well as ever in her life, full of the optimism the tubercular so often possess, and joy came with her to Chardon Place. Emerson's brothers, like himself, continued to prosper, to march forward on their chosen routes, although Edward must still be careful not to overtax himself. Now one and now another came to spend a few days in the little home. They all loved their sister-in-law, believed with Waldo that she was the fairest and best of her sex. There was good talk after the simple supper had been cleared away by the maid, a pleasant farmer's daughter from the Concord home. Charles was developing magnificently. He had a great sensitiveness to beauty, the beauty of nature, the beauty of words and of thought. He and Waldo ranged over things spiritual and things temporal in their conversation, and Waldo found that this young brother had a way of focusing attention on the essential quality of whatever attracted him. He saw the thing that mattered in any sort of clutter and could lift it into the general view with a phrase. There was an admirable humor in the lad, too, that delighted Waldo who, seldom heard to laugh, had an enchanting smile for what pleased him, a glimmer of mischief, a quiet but apt return of wit. Ruth and Ellen, sitting with their work, listened to the men, well content. Where the talk swung to music or poetry Ellen was drawn in, flushing a little, eager about a new piece she had found in one of the English reviews her husband took, running to fetch it, reading it out in her pretty voice. Or perhaps begging Waldo to read one of his own verses, which he willingly did, reminding Edward or Charles, as the case was, of the days when they used to repeat his stirring battle lines in the strenuous season of war.

Graver topics received attention during these evenings. More and more Waldo was beginning to find the established theological beliefs futile, even erroneous.

"It's time for a crusade against the dry-as-dusts," his brothers agreed. "And no one better than you to lead, to give out the new message, Waldo. You have all the young people behind you, those whose eyes are to the future. They feel you are right, and it is they who matter. Talk to them, talk for them. The trouble so far has been that only the old have had power; that a boy was no sooner out of college than the mouldy garments of the past were wrapped about him and the timeworn shibboleth put into his mouth."

Emerson nodded:

"The Bible tells us that the Lord our God is a living God," he said. "In the deadness of our theological hairsplitting we've forgotten that."

Autumn came with her blue skies, her burning hues, her dance of the winds; then snow fell and the cold grew more and more bitter. People kept to their houses, in the New England fashion, with double windows against the biting air, stoves burning night and day. Never a fresh gust let into the bedrooms, whose icy chill struck like a blow. The beds were warmed with long-handled brass contraptions full of hot coals swept between the sheets, and you lay under and on a feather bed. Christmas passed; New Year's was celebrated with family parties, mince pies and roast turkey. The Ripleys were guests at Chardon Place, and plans were laid for a visit next summer to the Old Manse by the Emersons, while the proposed repairs on the Old North were being made.

Then, without warning, Ellen had a hemorrhage.

Terrified preparations to take her south were interrupted by her physician. She must not attempt a journey just now, must not leave her bed.

This time there was no relenting.

Ellen went to meet her death with the simplicity, even the gentle cheerfulness with which she had lived. To her husband, hanging over her in an agony of helpless despair, she whispered that the Will of God was best, and the words came straight and true from her believing heart.

On February 13, 1831, Waldo set down in his journal this solitary sentence:

"Five days have wasted since Ellen went to Heaven to see, to know, to worship, to love, to intercede. Reunite us, O thou Father of our spirits."

Chapter VII

Europe

The question asked in the letter to Aunt Mary, "Can this hold?" had been answered. The year that opened in tragedy brought other blows. While Ellen was ill Edward had been stricken with the same disease and had accompanied a seafaring friend to Porto Rico, there to seek health if possible. There was, it appeared, no longer a question of his following the high path. He took an office position in a law office in the tropic isle in order to support himself, for he refused to be a burden on his family. Besides, he wrote them, it would help the days to pass, and the work was easy, well within his strength. As the summer wore on Ruth, whose heart ached at the grief in her son's face, at the silent endurance with which he met it, wrote Edward begging him to induce his brother to come down to spend a few months in that different scene. It might help him, she wrote, for as it was, she feared his health too would be affected. Edward was only too eager, and Waldo was almost on the point of yielding to the two when suddenly Charles had a breakdown. Overwork, too much strain; nothing worse yet, but get him away, said the doctor. Therefore it was he and not Waldo who sailed for Porto Rico.

Waldo was perhaps relieved so far as he was concerned. He did not wish to leave. There was work for him here, and he still felt near his lost wife while in the home they had shared. Hardly a day passed without his walking to the graveyard in Roxbury where Ellen's body lay. The man suffered profoundly, and his was not a spirit that could find relief in outer demonstration; not to any one could he speak his sorrow, but must wrestle within himself for victory over the immense depression and frightening sense of loss that possessed him. He did his work with church and congregation as he had done it in his happiness; nor did he doubt the goodness of God because Ellen had been taken from him. His faith was no rootless thing that must be fed with happiness or wither out of existence. Austere he seemed as, grave and kind, he carried out the manifold duties of his position; but there was nothing bitter, there was nothing of complaint. Only in his journal did he permit himself, and there not often, to express something of his trouble.

"*The spring*," he wrote, "*is wearing into summer, and life is wearing into death; our friends are forsaking us, our hopes are declining (while) the days go by, griefs, and simpers, and sloths, and disappointments. . . I know too well what is gone from me. .*"

As autumn came on he began to be increasingly uncertain that he had found his right place in life. Was he honest in remaining as a pastor of the church when so many doubts as to the worth of the church's rites assailed him? Was it well for him to administer offices that he felt to be mere hollow echoes from a mistaken past? These church ordinances were man-made; nor was he able to find in them any divine inspiration. During the winter he met the Swedenborgian minister, Dr. Worcester, and was greatly attracted by much in this faith, heretofore new to him. Samson Reed, a member of that church, whom he also met, had written a good deal about it, and Waldo studied these writings. Here was at least a voice of the greatest sincerity and a conception of Christianity distant indeed from Calvinism. He never entirely agreed with the Swedenborgian doctrines, but they helped to broaden his religious outlook and to free him finally from the old bonds. But that was for the future. Just now he was at grips with the necessity for making a personal decision.

In the beginning of his journal for the year 1832 he put down his growing conviction that it is "*the best part of man that revolts most against his being a minister. His good revolts from official goodness . . . the difficulty is that we do not make a world of our own but fall into institutions already made, and have to accommodate ourselves to them to be useful at all, and this accommodation is, I say, a loss of so much of integrity, and of course of so much of power.*"

Much snow and inclement weather had prevented Waldo for many weeks from taking his accustomed walk to Roxbury. When at length the walking became possible toward the last of March, he visited the vault again. Descending into it he opened the coffin and looked once more upon Ellen. This fact he entered in his journal, without any explanation or comment.

In June he called together a meeting of the Committeemen and told them that he wished to discontinue offering the Communion. Astounded, they demanded to know why he made such a request. His answer still more surprised them:

"It is considered as the most sacred of the institutions of the church, and I cannot go habitually to an institution which is esteemed as holiest with indifference or dislike," he explained. "I have no hostility to it as a rite, but I have no sympathy with it. If it were regarded simply as a rite of commemoration I could do so; but not as it is. If I were not called upon to administer it, I would not let my lack of sympathy obtrude itself, but to offer as the church's highest rite one in which I am not even interested is clearly out of the question."

Very naturally the church refused to give up Communion, one of the very foundation stones of its creed and hallowed by all the centuries of Christianity. Mr. Emerson must decide one way or the other. Either continue to fulfill that and the other rites, or resign.

Various friends with whom he discussed the position advised him to take time to consider the question thoroughly. July was at hand, and July was to be devoted to the delayed repairs, which should have been attended to the year before. Emerson decided to go to the White Mountains, there to come to a conclusion. He needed a change badly, and he would not be leaving his mother alone, for his brothers were both back from Porto Rico, Charles completely restored and Edward greatly improved, though it was clear he could not again hope for normal health.

Waldo stayed in New Hampshire through August, though he reached his decision within the first fortnight or so. It was, as might have been expected, to give up the pastorate. To say that his parishioners were amazed is hardly to express their feelings. There were many who declared he was certainly insane. Edward had been so, now it was Waldo. Could any man in his senses resign from the ministry of an important church like Old North with no better excuse than that he was "not interested" in the rite of Communion? He couldn't expect to find another church more accommodating! They listened to his farewell sermon, preached on September 9, shaking their heads and muttering. Such a thing had never happened before. What was the world coming to!

As for Emerson, he felt that a phase of life had come to an end. His youth, with its ambitions, his married happiness, his ministery – all over, sunk into the irremediable past. Where next should he turn, what do?

In October he stood beside his mother and his brother Charles watching the ship that was taking Edward back to Porto Rico climb over the horizon. So long as he could be distinguished

Edward stood on the deck, his gaze on the dwindling figures of those he loved, stood there until the last outline of his country sank into the sea. He knew he would never again return.

They knew it too. This blow, following on so many, staggered Waldo. In November Charles wrote to Aunt Mary:

"*Waldo is sick. His spirits droop; he looks to the south, and thinks he should like to go away. I never saw him so disheartened.*"

His health was not too good. All his plans had come to naught. He felt that everything lay behind him, and could hardly visualize a future. After some hesitations it was decided that Europe would be the best place in which to recuperate. In the end he wrote a letter of farewell to his church and sailed on December 30 in a vessel bound for Sicily.

Emerson was between twenty-nine and thirty years of age at this date. So far he had published nothing and beyond the circle of his immediate influence in Boston and its near-by towns and cities was practically unknown. Yet within that circle the Emerson name stood for much; belonged to the aristocracy of learning and position which then took the highest position in any New England community. The family was poor; it was unknown in politics; yet it had numbered men of notable power in each generation, men who had led their people along that moral pathway which, since the foundation of New England, had been the most honorable and important a man could take. There was no man worth the knowing in Boston with whom Waldo was not acquainted, few with whom he was not on fairly intimate terms. In going abroad he had it in mind to meet with leading literary men in the countries he expected to visit, especially England and Scotland, as well as to fraternize with the clergymen belonging to his faith. Letters to such men were offered to him by friends of his who were friends of theirs, and he also carried introductions to American consuls and ministers along his proposed route. His brother William wanted him to go to Germany, where he had made many friends, but for some reason Waldo made no plan to visit that country.

Crossing the Atlantic in winter was tough business a hundred and more years ago. The voyage took until February 3, when the packet finally came to anchor in Marsa Muschetta Harbor, Isle of Malta. Emerson had not enjoyed the trip in the plunging, rolling uncomfortable little vessel, the *Jasper*, a brig of 236 tons, laden with logwood, mahogany, tobacco, sugar, coffee, beeswax and cheese, a cargo that reads like a line from Masefield. He had suffered from seasickness and cold, and from boredom. There were five passengers besides himself, none of whom interested him. He found the captain, Ellis, and the mate more to his liking, fascinated as always by the man who was master of his job. The captain was a stout bluff seaman who read no book but the Bible, but this he knew almost by heart. To his great delight and Emerson's equally great surprise, he proved to his passenger that there was one book in the divine volume that did not once mention the name of God. As for the mate, he taught Waldo how to use a quadrant and much about the stars. But neither the captain's biblical lore nor the starry enthusiasms of the mate sufficed to make a sailor of Mr. Emerson. "Why," he asked himself in amazement, "did not the first man who ever went to sea put back at once and so make an end of the matter for all time? The Wind, the Wind, the Wind! It was utterly their master. If it stops we starve, if it blows too ferociously, we die."

Malta is a beautiful gateway to the old world, with its ancient churches and palaces and noble apartment houses built of the cool gray Maltese stone, its twisted narrow streets and picturesque squares. On the flat roofs of their dwellings the populace spend most of their leisure time, and in the streets where Emerson wandered for hours, unable, as he writes, to keep his eyes from rolling or his tongue from uttering exclamations of surprise and pleasure, all the peoples of the world met in a gaudy kaleidoscope of animated motion.

The New Englander presented his introductions to a Mr. Temple, the American preacher, and attended a service in the little chapel on the roof of Mr. Temple's three-story house; and to the consul, who took him to an evening party at the Governor's, a fancy dress affair that was very gay and amusing, in a magnificent setting of splendid century-old rooms, a setting so romantically lovely, Emerson thought, as to dwarf the party.

There was no lack of local color in those days. The little brigantine, with its grandiose name, *Il Santissimo Ecce Homo*, that took Waldo from Malta to Sicily, was like something out of a comic opera. Its rollicking crew and captain, on a perfect equality, sang, shouted and laughed the entire sixteen hours of the crossing; drank constantly from an open cask of blood-red wine conveniently placed on the deck; and burst into hilarious, if unintelligible comment at any word or gesture of the six Americans, for Emerson's five ship's companions had joined with him to hire the vessel. When the captain hunted up the gazetteer and read aloud to his attentive men what was said in that useful publication about Boston, that mythical city from which these strange wanderers had come, both he and his crew were so overtaken by amusement that they nearly strangled. In all the rest of his life put together, thought Emerson, he had not heard as much laughter as in the hours of this sea trip across the purple Mediterranean.

In Sicily he travelled muleback through scenery of a breathless beauty, where the mountain slopes were sheeted with flowers, and villages older than time slid down perilous slopes to golden or black beaches. Here were monasteries where robed friars had chanted for a thousand years; catacombs old when Christ was born; churches so exquisite the New England minister could hardly bear to leave each in its turn.

Emerson made the regulation Italian tour; Naples, Rome, Florence, followed each other; and though he admits he was "dazzled and drunk with beauty," he was also deeply shocked by the poverty, by the beggars who infested every street; who stood staring with hungry eyes in gaunt faces as he ate a meal on the terrace of a restaurant; who showed their sores and screamed their appeals before every renowned and visited place. He met a few distinguished Italians; had an audience with the Pope; and in Florence presented a letter to Walter Savage Landor, and was invited to dine at the poet's house, the Villa Ghirardesca. A fine house, full of pictures, but to Emerson's surprise containing not more than a dozen books. To his comment Landor answered that he always gave away his books, once he had read them, that those on hand were waiting to be read. The two men had "good and pleasant talk" together, and Emerson admired Landor's wife and four handsome children. Landor, himself a great man, sensed the greatness in his visitor and spoke of his impression to a friend; yet wondered what had brought the American minister to his doors.

The truth is that Emerson was seeking, as he wrote Aunt Mary, the wise man, the true friend, the finished character. He wished to meet the great teacher, with whom he might discuss the mysteries of man's moral nature, from whom he could hope to get answers to much that was disturbing him. He did not find this man, as he told his aunt, saying, "I never get used to men. They always awaken expectations in me which they always disappoint."

In Paris he found an old acquaintance, Oliver Wendell Holmes, with whom he went to a dinner given in honor of General Lafayette. But he did not remain long in France. He wanted to get to England, to the Old Home, the land from which every one of his ancestors had come. There were men he wanted to meet there; in particular one man, as yet but slightly known either in England or America. This was Thomas Carlyle. Before he knew his name Waldo had read with approval and interest the unsigned articles with their unmistakable quality, appearing from time to time in different reviews; and when finally the author made himself known he decided that here was one man he could not afford to miss. No one he knew had had any contact with Carlyle, nor could he discover so much as where he lived. But find him he would.

But his first objective was naturally London. Here he sought out John Stuart Mill, whose letters on "The Spirit of the Age" in the *Examiner* had caught his interest. Mill had beaten even the Emersons in the business of being educated, for by the time he was three he knew the Greek alphabet and strings of Greek words and was tackling other lines of study. Like Waldo he was deeply enthralled by the questions of moral and social philosophy, though his approach was not, as was Emerson's, from the religious side. At any rate, the two men found a good deal to say to each other, and Mill was able to give his new acquaintance a letter to Carlyle, without being able to tell him where to find that dour Scot, except that it must be somewhere in Scotland. He took the American to the House of Commons, however, where Emerson listened to the debates with enjoyment.

But summer was well on its way, and as the return home was scheduled for the end of August the American wanted to waste no more time before reaching Edinburgh. He had accepted the invitation to preach there from Dr. John Gairner, pastor at the Unitarian Chapel, and carried a letter to the doctor; but it was Alexander Ireland, a young man who occupied a position of some importance in the chapel, who met Emerson, in the doctor's unavoidable absence, and with whom he at once began a friendship that endured for life. "Luckily for me the Doctor was occupied elsewhere," the young man wrote to a friend, "and thus I became an entertainer of angels unawares." Never before, declares Ireland, "have I met anyone of so fine and varied a culture, and with such frank sincerity of speech. A refined and delicate courtesy, a kind of mental hospitality, so to speak—the like of which, or anything approaching which, I have never before encountered—seem to be a part of his very nature, inseparable from his daily walk and conversation." After hearing Emerson deliver his sermon he adds that the "pregnant thought and serene self-possession of the young Boston minister had a greater charm for me than all the rhetorical splendors of Chalmers." The entire congregation apparently shared Ireland's pleasure, listening to Mr. Emerson with a flattering attention, and remaining to shake him by the hand while expressing their interest in what he had said. He received these praises with an unaffected sincere modesty that further pleased the Scotch gathering. Perhaps, in that distant northern city, Waldo felt more at home than anywhere since leaving his native town.

Ireland, luckily, was able to inform his new friend where to find Carlyle. The Carlyles, Thomas and Jane, had been in Edinburgh earlier in the year, where Thomas was gathering the material for his article "The Diamond Necklace," which marked the beginning of his interest in the French Revolution. He had also had "*Sartor Resartus*" accepted by *Fraser's Magazine*, but its publication in that periodical had been received, so the editor later informed the writer, "with unqualified dissatisfaction."

"He was considerably disheartened at that, Mr. Emerson," Ireland said. "So much so that he decided to return to a little farm, Craigenputtock, where the pair have been living for the past five years. It's a lonely spot, and it's a hard life they lead there, and I think it'll be a pleasant thing for Mr. Carlyle to receive your visit."

It proved a pleasant thing for both Carlyle and Emerson.

Emerson's wish that he might meet a friend to whom he should be drawn instantly and wholly, as he had been to Ellen, was fulfilled. And Carlyle was not only greatly flattered by the visit of this young American divine, coming over thousands of miles to seek him out, but deeply attracted to him. The two tramped the heather together, talking, all that afternoon, and for most of the night before the fire in the study, for Carlyle would not hear of his visitor leaving before the next day. Jane ministered to them, but that done, left them to each other. Carlyle was a marvellous talker, full of passion, enthusiasm, invective, scorn; Emerson was a perfect listener. They were entirely different from each other, yet there was at once and always a singularly real sympathy between them. In moral integrity, in unfaltering sincerity, in mental calibre they were equal; and they loved each other through the rest of their lives, probably all the better because they rarely met, so that the differences of temperament that might have proved a barrier in close contact had no power, while the essential qualities that ruled each remained clear and binding. Emerson was somewhat disappointed in not finding the guide he had hoped for, but he found what was better, the companion to his own spirit. While Carlyle, writing Lord Houghton soon after the visit, said that he did not know what had brought Emerson, but that, when he left, "I watched him climb the hill that would take him out of sight, but I didn't go with him to see him descend. I preferred to watch him mount and vanish like an angel."

So twice while in Scotland Emerson had been likened to an angel!

Stopping on his way to Liverpool to see Wordsworth, Coleridge, Southey, to all of whom he had letters, he was not so deeply impressed. The visit was brief, a few hours only, and Emerson had never cared very greatly for the poetry of the Lake School. Whatever talk there was did not discover to Emerson the greatness of these men. He appraises the effect upon himself in these words:

"Upon an intelligent man, wholly a stranger to their names, they would make in conversation no deep impression,—none of a world-filling fame. They would be remembered as sensible, earnest, well-read men; not more. Especially . . . are they deficient . . . in insight into religious truth. They have no idea of that species of moral truth which I call the first philosophy."

It is an interesting judgment in that it reveals Emerson's own preoccupations. He was too entirely engaged in his own struggle to find definitions for that species of truth he called the first philosophy, to have time or inclination to follow other men in their search for what should satisfy them. Less and less was he to find an answer to his questions in men's talk or in their books.

During this European journey he had begun to put into shape material for his own first book, which he called *Nature.* It would not be published for almost another three years, but it was in the making. He had come to his true work. On the voyage home he confided to his journal that "I like my book about Nature." Furthermore, he set down these convictions:

"Man begins to hear a voice that fills the Heavens and the earth, saying that God is within him. I find this amazing revelation of my immediate relation to God a solution of all the doubts that oppressed me. I recognize the distinction of the outer and inner self; the double consciousness that within this erring, passionate, mortal self sits a supreme, calm, immortal

mind, whose power I do not know; but it is stronger than I; it is wiser than I; it never approved me in wrong; I seek counsel of it in my doubt; I repair to it in my dangers; I pray to it in my undertakings. It seems to me the face which the Creator uncovers to his child."

The months of travel had borne their fruit. But Emerson came home with relief. He wanted his own country about him. He had written to William "my own study is the best place for me." Yet during that more than eight months of absence he had reached spiritual and mental maturity; he had, as we now say, found himself. He came back not knowing where he would live, nor how he would live, but certain that, as he declared, "God will show me!"

Chapter VIII

Home at Last

"God will show me." It was in this faith that Ralph Waldo returned to his country. Amazingly that faith was justified.

During his absence abroad his mother-in-law, Mrs. Kent, had died. Met on the pier at New York by his brother, William, he heard that the lady's estate had been left to him, and that he could count on twelve hundred dollars a year. His financial anxieties were solved, at least for the present. The few debts he had incurred could be paid off at once, he would not be forced back into the uncongenial role of school-teacher in order to support himself. Also he had time to consider his future work. What was he to do? The genius within him was pressing for expression. He felt that he had something of value to tell his brother man, that he must be about his Father's business, not in the orthodox fashion of the day, but in harmony with those convictions over which he had brooded on the voyage back and whose outlines he had jotted down in his journal.

He joined his mother, who was living with her sister and brother-in-law, the Mr. and Mrs. Ladd who had welcomed Waldo to their farm at Newton after his breakdown at the Divinity School. Here he would stay until he had definitely decided upon his future course. One plan he had in mind was to buy a small place in the bracing climate of the Berkshires; get Edward to live with him there, supposing it possible to rescue the lost, beloved brother from his long martyrdom in Porto Rico; gather one or two interesting men about them, and establish a magazine in which all the new thought of the day should get free expression, where articles by Carlyle, Alexander Ireland, John Stuart Mill and other writers in England, as well as native talent, could be printed. Edward was all enthusiasm, wrote that he had been improving in health, felt sure that with the coming of spring he could safely return.

Meanwhile, no sooner was Emerson back than his church, Old North, sent him an invitation to preach the coming Sunday. He accepted, and pleased the crowded congregation so much that several influential men begged him to reconsider his resignation. Could he not resume his pastorate?

But Emerson was more than ever opposed to undertaking the routine duties of a minister's career; not there lay his road. He would preach, and gladly, for any church that wanted him, but only on condition that he could say what he chose. As for religious rites, they were not for him. Freedom he must have, freedom was what he wished for others. It speaks well for the new breadth of vision in the church of that day that he was accepted on these conditions. For four years to come he rarely missed a Sunday preaching to a congregation in some New England church, either in Boston or one of the towns within a day's reach by the stage. As before he found his greatest welcome coming from the younger people among those who heard him. They sought him out at the end of the service to tell him how much his talk had meant; he had spoken what they had dimly thought, what they had been fumbling for without knowing how to reach it. He clarified for these youths and maidens the murky atmosphere of doubt through which they could no longer find their way, sweeping the fog of dogma out of window with clear, bright phrases that set the sun back in heaven.

But it was with the beginning of 1834 that Emerson started the particular work that was to occupy the greater part of his time from then on, and to make his name known not only all over America, but in Britain. He began it unsuspectingly enough. The Massachusetts Natural History Society asked whether, for the customary fee, he would lecture for them on his foreign travels.

Emerson was interested. He had pages of notes, the subject was fresh in his mind, and it would be a new experience to speak out of a pulpit. He gave the lecture, and his success was immediate. So much so that he at once began to receive other invitations from learned societies, such as the American Institute of Instruction, the Society for the Diffusion of Useful Knowledge, the Mechanics Institute. Wherever he was heard he charmed his audience and he made it think, and Boston audiences liked to be made to think. He spoke not only on Europe as he had seen it, but on popular science, and on literature, especially on biography.

Between preaching and lecturing Emerson found himself fully occupied. The book he had spoken of as "liking," *Nature*, was laid aside until the summer. Though the lectures were confined to Boston, his Sundays continued to be spent at different towns. In February he went to Plymouth to preach in the Unitarian church there. He had not done so before, but the congregation was so pleased with him that he was invited to return the following month. On this return visit he was asked to dine at the house of a lady he had met the month before, Miss Lydia Jackson, a few months older than himself. Here he met her brother, a young doctor of great promise, a man of wit and intelligence. There were two or three other guests, the best people of Plymouth; talk was good, the whole atmosphere delightful. Lydia herself had a sweet dignity, a seriousness tempered by humor, a kind of unworldly serenity that had won her the nickname of Abbess among her friends. Emerson found himself talking to her more freely than was his wont, he who preferred always to listen. He had recently heard from Edward that there was little chance of his being able to come north, and the magazine plan had been given up. He spoke to her of this disappointment, and there was healing in her gentle sympathy. She did not say much, but what she said had the wisdom of understanding, and Emerson went away feeling that he had found a friend, promising to return soon.

In April the first railway train to move in New England was run from Boston to Worcester, and Emerson was one of the distinguished company, which included the governor, to ride upon it. Just as the first automobiles resembled carriages, so the first railway cars looked like coaches, and rolled along with a tremendous amount of rattle and shake. "Men, trees and barns whizz by you as fast as the leaves of a dictionary," writes Emerson, an odd metaphor but a natural one for a man who must frequently spin through such pages on the search for an exact definition. And he goes on, "As our tea-kettle hissed along through a field of mayflowers we could judge of the sensations of a swallow who skims by trees and bushes with about the same speed. The very permanence of matter seems compromised and oaks, fields, hills, hitherto esteemed figures of tranquillity, do absolutely dance before you."

That summer Emerson's grandmother, Mrs. Ezra Ripley, died, and in September the old Doctor, now in his nineties, invited Waldo and his mother to make their home at the Old Manse with him. Charles also was to live there. He was reading law in the office of Judge Hoar, and engaged to the Judge's daughter Elizabeth, a fascinating young woman with a brilliant mind; Emerson already loved her as a sister, and the prospect of a close companionship with his brother Charles gave him happiness. Directly after his wife's death Dr. Ripley had written Waldo to say "Though the bond that united us is broken I hope you and your brothers will not cease to come to this house. You will not like to be excluded, and I shall not like to be neglected." Emerson copied this into his journal with the comment, "No better words could have been sent." They made it the easier to accept the old man's invitation; the more because a woman was needed at the Manse, and Ruth was already beloved there.

During the first week in October, a year since he had returned from Europe, Madam Emerson and Waldo settled themselves in the old homestead. From then on to the end Concord would be Emerson's home.

On the eighteenth of the month news arrived that Edward had died on the first. Waldo felt this death deeply, although he was glad that "Edward's fervid heart would suffer no longer." To this "brother of the bright and blazing star . . . all, all was given and only health denied."

The loss of Edward drew Waldo and Charles closer. The difference in their ages was no longer a barrier now that Charles was mature. He was an extraordinarily brilliant man, with a keen perception of all that was finest in nature, in literature, in human values. His memory was phenomenal; Waldo said of him that he seemed never to have forgotten anything that struck his mind, and that he could lay hold on whatever he wanted from this rich store instantly. The two brothers enjoyed long walks together in Concord's woods and fields and to Waldo it seemed that all he looked on had a fresher significance because Charles was with him, that this younger brother saw deeper into nature's heart, marked more of her various beauty than he had ever been able to do.

Waldo went to Plymouth for Christmas; he came back engaged to Lydia. This was not unexpected, for not only had Emerson gone to Plymouth more and more often with summer and fall, but Lydia had been invited to the Old Manse, where everyone approved of her. Satisfaction at the engagement was complete. With the coming of winter Emerson began in Boston a series of lectures on famous men, great men, the *Representative Men* of the volume of essays to be published years later. These lectures, and others to be given, increased his income appreciably, and he decided to build a house for himself and his bride, a house large enough too for Charles and Elizabeth when they married. At first Lydia had suggested that he and she live in her own Plymouth home, but Emerson decided against this. He admitted that Plymouth had as lovely a setting, had as fine sunsets, all that he wanted in a home; but in Concord he was happiest, his roots were there, the memories of boyhood days, ancestral claims.

Through the winter and early spring he and Charles, taking their walks, looked over possible sites for the house.

"It must be on a hill and face west," Waldo said.

"And with a glimpse of water," added Charles.

Dr. Ripley, interested in the home plan, offered them land he owned on the slope of a westward-facing hill, which overlooked the valley toward the Wachusett and Monadnock mountains. Both brothers agreed that nothing better could be found.

But when Waldo began to get estimates on the sort of house he wanted, with room for the two couples and for Ruth, he felt that the cost was too high. A house not properly built would be worse than no house. He began to look about, and when, in July, at an unexpected bargain, the Coolidge house at the opposite end of Concord on the Lexington Road was offered him, he bought. It was a very good house in excellent repair, though he would have to make some alterations before it would meet his requirements. He wrote to William that, compared with the fine hill site he and Charles had wanted, the house was in "a mean place," but that this would be improved with the trees he intended to set out, with the garden Lydia was planning to plant, and that anyhow he was going to fill the new home with "so many books, and papers and wise friends that it would have all the wit it could carry." There were two acres of ground and behind the meadows ran down to Mill Brook, while a path and footbridge led to Walden Pond, one of his favorite walks. On the whole he was well content, and so was Charles.

On September 12 of this year, 1835, Concord celebrated the one hundred and ninety-fifth anniversary of its foundation by the Emerson ancestor, stout old Peter Bulkeley. Emerson had consented to make the address on the occasion. With characteristic thoroughness he prepared for this speech not only by studying the Concord archives and historical papers in Cambridge, but by interviewing every old timer still to be found above ground. Many of these ancient relics sat on the platform with him when he spoke. Several of the old men had been among the minute men who had fought in Concord's famous battle that signalled the outbreak of the Revolution; and one of them might well have fired that shot which Emerson, in a poem not yet written, was to describe as the "shot heard round the world."

Two days later he drove from the new house, where all was made ready, to marry Lydia in Plymouth. The wedding was held in her own house, before a small gathering of intimate friends and relatives. Two days later the married pair drove back again through the glowing autumn in the sweet September sunshine to begin the long and happy life they were to have together. As they drew up before the gate of the front garden the candles Ruth had lighted ready for their welcome glimmered through the windows, softly beckoning them home. The man from the livery stable, who had been waiting, stepped forward to assist them to dismount, but Emerson motioned him aside and himself helped his wife to the ground. Hand in hand the two walked up the path and through the door flung open for them.

"This is now a home, not merely a house, Lydian," her husband said, as he closed the door behind them.

He had thus changed her name on the wedding day from Lydia to Lydian, to make it go more euphoniously with the Emerson.

On the morrow he set down this resolution:

"Henceforth I design not to utter any speech, poem or book that is not peculiarly my own work."

Chapter IX

The Shining Mark

Emerson's house was a simple expression of the New England Colonial, foursquare, of wood painted white; depending for its beauty on its proportions, on the fine spacing of door and windows, the slight ornament of grooved framing, the porch, the chimneys. These New England houses were admirably suited to their setting and to the people who lived in them. They had dignity and character. There was nothing superfluous and there was nothing skimped. Their old-fashioned gardens and fine trees became them, the bricked, box-bordered paths, the white paled fences with their neat gates.

A broad hall with doors at either end ran through the house. On entering by the front door, Emerson's study was the first room on the right, with the parlor beyond, farther down the hall. On the left was first a bedroom and then the dining-room. The kitchen extended back from this, in the L, with woodshed and pantry. Above were more bedrooms and the new, still unfinished study added for Charles. The stairway led up on the left side of the hall.

The downstairs doors were of the pattern known as Christian. A Christian door has its upper and larger portion divided into four panels by a broad cross, the upright being longer than the crossbar. The rooms were square, the ceilings neither low nor high, excellently planned to give just the right impression of space and comfortableness. The windows too were of exactly the right size, and each had its cushioned seat.

Ruffled white sash curtains were caught back by muslin loops, outer curtains of a deep warm red hung straight to the floor. This pleasant, glowing red upholstered a sofa and two fine chairs that had once belonged to Lydian's mother, and which she placed in her husband's study. Here too was the tall bookcase made for the bride by a Plymouth cabinetmaker. The maple center table with its three carved feet had belonged to Ellen. On it stood a lamp in the shape of a Grecian urn, with a round frosted glass globe, a few large books, and the lapboard Emerson wrote on, with the inkstand and quill pen beside it. A wooden rocker with red cushions, between table and window, was his writing chair; he never used a desk.

Thick smooth carpets of a sage green, with a small pattern, covered the downstairs rooms, hall and stairway. The walls were butter-colored. This scheme of rich red, cool green and delicate yellow governed the lower floor of the house. Black marble framed the fireplaces and made the mantels. Bright brass firedogs and fender gleamed in the study, and Waldo loved tending the fire. Through the cold weather it was always his last act before going up to bed to place the fragments of wood that still smoldered carefully back on the hearth and to lay over them a coat of ashes that would hold a heart of fire until the morning.

Engravings and family portraits were hung on the walls. Between the windows long, narrow mirrors framed in gold gave back the quiet charm of the rooms. In the study a mirror was also hung over the fireplace, and Carlyle's wedding present, a very fine colored copy of the famous Aurora by Guido Reni, with an inscription in Carlyle's hand, decorated one side of the room, flanked by engravings of two of Michelangelo's Sybils, which Emerson had brought back from Europe. More bookcases besides the Plymouth one made rich the walls with classical tomes in leather bindings, and various small souvenirs and knickknacks were gathered on the mahogany shelves of a corner whatnot. A pleasant room, the study, as all the rooms were pleasant, were serene. There was nothing machine-made, nothing ostentatious; all gave the effect of being loved, not only by the owners, but by the makers.

The pattern of life in the new home was soon established, for little as Waldo liked routine in thought, he preferred it in daily existence. An ordered round, fixed habits of work and relaxation, these were a release to freedom of thought, becoming as they must almost as unconscious of effort as breathing or digestion.

Directly after breakfast Emerson went to his study, there to work until the dinner hour at one of the clock. His pad on his knees, his papers and books on the table beside him, able to glance out of the window across his lawn toward the road as he mused over his work, he could hear, without being disturbed, the quiet life of the house going forward beyond his closed door. The light step of Lydian a mere murmur on the carpet, a door softly shut, a whisper of broom or dustcloth, a voice faintly coming from the more distant region of the kitchen, these were all.

He was working hard. He had promised the Masonic Temple in Boston a course of ten weekly lectures in which he was to expound his philosophic ideas. Furthermore he had accepted an offer to preach every Sunday at a church in East Lexington, a service he rendered for the next three years with few interruptions. Lectures and sermons must therefore be prepared; more than this, he was working over the final copy of his book, *Nature*. In all this work he was developing his own ideas, following no man, seeking truth, and the meaning of life, and the worth of beauty. He was breaking the way to a new conception of individual value and responsibility. Stuff like that is not to be hastily or carelessly created.

Often there would be a guest or two for the dinner, with cheerful conversation. Lydian was a hostess born and liked nothing better than to have a congenial man or woman who would amuse and interest her husband. She was wise and knew he must be lured from overdoing, have his thoughts swung from the morning work to fresh topics. As long as the weather permitted he spent a part of every afternoon in the vegetable garden; he was awkward at such matters, often he made mistakes she quietly corrected unbeknownst to him. The great thing was to get him working out-of-doors. Already the trees set out when the place had been bought were promising well; pines and chestnuts that would delightfully frame the house in time. Lydian herself was a passionate and skillful gardener, and before winter drew in had already done great things in the flower garden back of the house. She had brought slips, roots, bulbs from her Plymouth home and set these out, replanted the beds and borders, put in flowering shrubs. Whenever she was not to be found about the house you had only to go into the garden to find her happily at work, and in the years to come her roses, lilies and pinks, her sweet peas and sweet williams, all the lovely company of garden glory were famous in the village, while her many friends benefited from the generous overflow of plants or cut flowers or carefully gathered seeds.

Charles, still at the Old Manse, came in often to join his brother in one of the long, leisurely walks they loved and which took them to the many beauty spots on hillside or by the river, through the woods to Walden, to the hemlocks whose dark grace made beautiful the cliffs where the river took a noble bend under high bluffs. In these walks Waldo found in Charles the perfect, the inspiring companion, the intimacy between the two men having grown steadily now they were within daily contact. There must have been a great fascination about Charles. He was singularly handsome, with that look of race which was a family trait, that pride of beaiing as innate as it was unconscious. He had a quick and rippling humor that enchanted all who knew him, and there was an ardor, a flame in him which Waldo missed in himself and loved the more in his brother. Charles was to marry Elizabeth in the coming September, when he would be admitted to the bar. Their apartment in the Emerson house was being completed through the winter of 1835-36, and already they were choosing its furnishings. Elizabeth was like a daughter to Ruth, who had come to live permanently with Waldo in December, when Dr. Ripley's son, Samuel, with Sarah his wife, could come to the Old Manse. Samuel was to take over much of the church work from the hale old nonogenarian, and Sarah of course would run the Manse.

Emerson had been made hog reever according to a time-honored rule in Concord. Being hog reever meant that for a year the newly married resident of the village must hold himself in readiness to rush forth at call and chase escaped pigs out of gardens and cornlots back to their own ground or to the public pen to be called for by the owner, who must pay damages should there have been any. Nothing amused his wife, nor Charles and Elizabeth, so much as to see Waldo, long staff clutched in his hand, dash out to the job with an air of importance Charles declared he never put on for a lecture. Emerson from the first entered completely into Concord's life. There were, as men who knew him frequently said, two Emersons: one the dreamer, the philosopher, the man of genius; the other the homely country villager, fulfilling a dozen duties, hobnobbing with farmers and tradesman, joining the fire brigade, with his axe and leather bucket hanging conveniently by the back door to be snatched as he ran; taking his place on school and library committees, and making an important member of the Social Circle, a club consisting of twenty-five Concord men who represented the professions, the trades, the farmers, mechanics and other interests of the township. This club met on Tuesday evenings, throughout the six winter months, and Emerson never missed a meeting it was possible for him to attend. He liked these shrewd, sensible, solid men; he delighted in their forthright speech. He used to say in later years that the talk he listened to in that club was, to what he heard at Harvard meetings, as solid land compared to a wafer. These village folk were interested in realities and had learned common sense at their work, and what they said came from personal experience, not by way of books and hearsay. Beginning as he had in a world bounded by books, Emerson never lost his love for them; but of their importance as the bread of life he became more and more doubtful. In his first book, which would be ready for the publisher that spring, it was to nature he bade his readers go for truth and for guidance, not to the printed word.

The stage passed his house and once a week he climbed into it and was off for Boston and his weekly lecture. Among his hearers were the Peabodys, a family with whom Emerson had established a very real friendship during his pastorate at Old North. The lecture over, he frequently went back with them for supper and the spare room was always at his service should he decide to stay the night. The older daughter, Elizabeth, was a woman of considerable culture and very wide reading, quite capable of interesting Emerson in her judgments of literary or philosophic matters, while her youngest sister Sophia, though something of an invalid, was an engagingly lovely and happy-spirited girl for whom Waldo felt a marked affection. She was an artist in a small way and had her studio with its north light, its easels, canvases, painty smell, its copies of the old masters brought to her from abroad by traveled friends; and in this room a group of her Boston acquaintance liked to gather of an evening for an hour or two of chat. Three brothers and another sister, Mary, swelled the family count at this time, but two of the boys did not live to maturity. It was one of those families where everyone is interesting and interested in many things, and Emerson liked the atmosphere of affectionate camaraderie that ruled the house. The day was to come when Sophia would marry Nathaniel Hawthorne and make her home, too, in Concord.

Winter was going; the calendar if not the weather told that spring had climbed over the southern rim of the world on her way north. The last snows were gone with April, but cold rains and winds kept everyone shivering. It had been a wonderful winter, well packed with work and happiness. Charles was looking forward to entering politics and hoped to serve his state well; no young man was better fitted for such labor. Waldo had been invited to give another series of lectures in Salem, once the Boston series was finished, and as the weather was so bad and there were two lectures a week, he had decided to stay in that city for the first week or even longer unless the rains stopped and the roads improved.

The day after his first lecture, however, a letter was brought to him. It was from Ruth and written in great anxiety. Charles was ill. He was running a high fever, seemed weak, was coughing. Could Waldo take the stage back and help them decide what it was best to do?

Though he came at once Charles had suffered a bad collapse before he arrived and Dr. Bartlett, friend as well as physician, advised a trip south if it could be managed. Charles soon recovered astonishingly from this collapse, and was quite sure all the excitement about his condition was unwarranted; but he yielded to the general alarm, especially when Elizabeth, composed though so white she startled Waldo when she came into the room, begged him to go. She did not say "for my sake," but she looked it.

It was a four day journey by stage to New York, where the

first stop was to be made at William's house. Ruth and the two brothers started on April 22, the weather still inclement, but Charles made the trip comfortably, full as ever of interest in what went on about him, amused at the small incidents of the journey. Waldo sent a letter back from one of the inns where they halted at night to say he did not think Charles was really ill: "not seriously ill, otherwise than that he has a very delicate system, with very little power of resistance."

William had himself married during the past year, and lived in a comfortable little house on a cross street not very far from the City Hall. Charles seemed so very much better, and Susan, the new sister-in-law, had arranged everything so admirably for the sick man that it was decided he and his mother would stay there for the present. If he did not mend as quickly as now appeared likely, Waldo would take him and Ruth farther south. Meanwhile there was that lecture course waiting in Salem! Waldo went back to Salem, reaching there May 2. He felt the more easy to do so since belated spring had suddenly arrived in warmth and sunshine.

Charles went on getting better, helped by his natural cheerfulness. On May 9, a balmy, delicious day, he wanted to go outdoors. William procured a carriage, an open Victoria, and with Ruth beside him Charles was driven uptown to the green fields of Harlem. On the drive Ruth persuaded him to consent to go south for the next month. Since he was so much stronger she felt sure that she could manage without Waldo's help, and a few weeks of rest in Richmond would be sure to restore him completely.

"All right, Mother, if you can take me, we'll go at once. I feel strong enough for any journey and in such weather the trip will be a delightful excursion. Waldo ought not to leave his lectures nor his home, and I don't want him break his engagements for my sake. If it will satisfy your anxieties to have me south for awhile, so let it be. I suppose if I returned to Concord I couldn't help working," he smiled at her, "and you know Waldo insists that that is the Emerson curse, not knowing how to idle."

They reached William's home in good spirits. Charles descended, and gave his hand to his mother to help her out. Susan had seen them coming and was at the door to welcome them back. Charles mounted the porch steps and entered. He turned to say something, staggered, reeled toward the stairs and sank to the floor. When they reached his side he was unconscious.

William, answering Ruth's agonized cry, came running from upstairs. He picked his brother up, felt a shiver pass through him, carried him up to his bedroom and laid him on the bed.

Before the doctor could arrive Charles, without regaining consciousness, had quietly slipped from this world.

It seemed incredible to his family, for Charles had been so full of life, so eager in his hopes, so ready for a future that was opening with every promise of success and happiness. Gone in a moment. They had realized that he was as Waldo had written, of a delicate constitution, but this. . . This shining mark for Death!

Waldo had suffered with Edward's death, but there was not the same sense of waste and sudden calamity as with this youngest and most beloved brother. There was Elizabeth too.

Elizabeth was wonderful. Her loss was irreparable, but she did not let it break her. She kept herself isolated for a week or more after the funeral, but when again she moved among her friends it was without complaint, without appeal for pity. With all the energy of her nature she turned to help others who needed help. She visited the poor and the sick, but she did not confine herself to these reliefs. She took up her studies, her reading, her intercourse with the friends she loved. She made it a point to see much of Ruth, to make Ruth feel that in her she still had a daughter. She and Waldo walked together, sought in the growing beauty of the year an answer to their grief, spoke simply of the beloved being who had left them.

"I would rather have this grief at the loss of Charles to bear, Waldo," the girl told him, "than never to have known what it was to be loved by him, never to have loved him in return. Shall I not be grateful for what I had, and not basely refuse to be happy over my happiness, the happiness he and I knew in each other? Waldo, that happiness is immortal: death cannot take it away."

He nodded, in his face a heavenly kindness. Here was courage, here was truth. Death was no end. Charles, all Charles had meant to them, was with them still. Man was not built of the fleeting appearances of time and change, nor was love set in those quicksands. Childhood, boyhood, youth, age, all fled by, but the man himself remained, and death was only another change.

"*The World rolls round,— mistrust it not,*
Befalls again what once befell,
All things return, both sphere and mote,
And I shall hear my bluebird's note,
And dream the dream of Auburn dell."

He wrote the lines, and turned his face to the future with the serene confidence in good that was never to fail him. Life was far more than happiness; it compassed God himself.

Chapter X

Freedom Boundless

Sometime during 1835 Emerson wrote Carlyle that a "group of young men" were contemplating the publication of a journal to be called "*The Transcendentalist*," and this is apparently the first time that the word was used in New England to designate a particular trend of thought and plan of progress. The plan went no further at the moment, but the ideals and ideas behind it continued to flourish and to define themselves.

These young men were certainly among an increasing number of persons, both men and women, who, not content with listening to Emerson lecture, wanted a closer touch with the man himself. Emerson was now at the beginning of his greatness; his genius was finding its proper expression, his marvellous power to climb to the very heights of idealism by way of the plain and homely factors of man's daily life was already making itself felt. There was, and there is no other word for it, a heavenliness about Ralph Waldo Emerson, and the words he brought to his hearers seemed hewn from a divine substance. Those gem-like sentences, those epigrammatic phrases not only spoke his own genius, but woke genius in the hearts of those who heard them. Men felt great and free as he "acquainted them first hand with Deity," went forth from the hall where they had sat into a world whose very sticks and stones were transmuted into precious substance.

Little wonder then that the white house in Concord became the Mecca for those whose imagination he had so fired, nor that youth led the way to it. For the time had come at last when Emerson, who, as his uncle Samuel Ripley had told him so many years back, had been disliked by the young and admired by the old, was to reverse the situation. Not that all older folk disagreed with him by any means; but it was the young men and the young women of his day who gave him a swift and ardent response, who saw in him the Captain of their choice, the man who held up to them an ideal worth living for, whose cry, "The old is for slaves. Go alone!" set their feet on a path that every generous and adventurous impulse urged them to climb.

Nor was ever man more hospitable to the appeal of youth, more patient with its fumbling, or quick to catch its flashes of insight, its fine dedications. In the afternoons that became more and more a regular institution, an event of each week, Emerson welcomed his "group of young men" not only into his study but into his mind. He answered their questions when he had an answer; spoke to them from the fund of wisdom within him; roused in them always the desire for a freer and a deeper life, a closer harmony with the God-inspired spirit within them that was his own aim and desire. And, the hour over, certain among the little company would adjourn to the parlor and to tea with Lydian and such Concord friends as chose to drop in. Then serious topics were set aside, Emerson's chuckle answered the neighborhood gossip, the amusing comments of Elizabeth Hoar, Mrs. Thoreau's lively chatter that kept time to her bobbing cap ribbons; or he discussed with Ephraim Bull from across the way his experiments with grapes, experiments that were to result in the creation of that famous Concord grape whose luscious purple clusters are today familiar from the Atlantic to the Pacific. Others came to add variety of comment and character; Elizabeth Peabody from Boston, chuckfull of philosophy and philanthropy, urging succor for the Indians; Margaret Fuller, who had just become acquainted with the Emersons, and who was teaching languages in a Boston school, and already visioning the emancipation of women, their higher education and wider opportunities. She herself had been trained by her father, a lawyer in Cambridgeport, was well-taught in Latin by the time she was six, and had scarcely reached her teens when she declared her favorite authors to be no less than Shakespeare, Cervantes and Molière. An even better Latin scholar and a master of Greek was another of these afternoon visitors, Sarah, Mrs. Samuel Ripley, mother of George, the cousin with whom Emerson usually stayed on his visits to Boston. Mrs. Ripley's learning was prodigious, varied and unexpected, but there was nothing of the pedant in her, as there was in Margaret. She was extremely entertaining and very much alive, and a great favorite with Ralph Waldo. Alcott, still living a wandering life before finally settling in Concord, used to turn up from time to time, brimming with schemes of a remarkable impracticality on which he could hold forth with an almost endless fluency. Emerson, imperturbable, kindly, amused, saw that every one was comfortable; listened more than he spoke; smiled on his friends with that smile which, so Sophia Hawthorne once said, was an unforgettable delight.

On July 4, 1836, Concord celebrated, more than a year late, the sixtieth anniversary of the Battle of Lexington. The delay had been caused by the failure to complete the setting up of the granite shaft raised to mark the heroic day of April 19, 1775.

Emerson had been asked to write an ode for the occasion which should be sung by the village choir. The lines he composed have since become familiar as far as the shot itself, celebrated in one flashing line in the first verse, later to be carved on the statue of the Minute Man:

"By the rude bridge that arched the flood,
Their flag to April's breeze unfurled,
Here once the embattled farmers stood,
And fired the shot heard round the world."

Only a month later Concord might well have fêted an event of which, as a community, it took no notice whatever. This was the publication of Emerson's first book, *Nature*, and the only one, except for his two volumes of poetry, not made up from his lectures. This was the book he had begun on his trip abroad and of which he had spoken of being pleased as he reread the first draft on the voyage home, almost three years before. During that time he had put much work on it, going to his crowded notebooks for illustrations and ideas. Once an idea came he would set it down in the form of a note, and later take it with him to brood upon in long solitary walks amid the nature that spoke to him a various language, from which he drew so much of his inspiration and which he felt to be the outermost garment of Divinity. All he spoke or wrote grew thus, from the notes set down at random; seeds that were left to wait their time for sprouting, and finally brought to full bloom by a long and careful process of development and expansion. When finally he handed *Nature* to the publishers he knew that it expressed the truth that was in him, and was undisturbed by the adverse criticisms of the very few critics who noticed it at all. How few its readers were one realizes when it is remembered that in twelve years only five hundred copies were sold!

The next event affecting Emerson this same year was an outcome of the celebration by Harvard of her two hundredth anniversary. All of her sons who could possibly manage it thronged to this jubilee, Emerson among them. He had been asked by George Ripley to go home with him for the night after the show was over, and a few other graduates dropped in for supper.

During the evening the group discussed the events of the day, and they had plenty of criticism for the stale and stuffy talk, the outworn ideals of the greater part of the program.

"Couldn't we form a nucleus that would attract the many who are seeking means of bringing about a new era in human thought and endeavor?" Emerson asked. He spoke of the idea for a magazine that had been suggested to him.

"A magazine might come later," replied Theodore Parker, who was one of the guests, "but it takes money to bring out an effective publication, and time as well. Why not begin with an organization that can meet informally at various members' houses, there to discuss possibilities and work out plans for future action?"

The idea seemed a good one and before the evening ended it was decided to call such a meeting in the same place ten days hence to which the persons most likely to be interested should be invited.

On the nineteenth of September, accordingly, more than a dozen men and women met together at the Ripley house. Theodore Parker, James Freeman Clarke, Bronson Alcott, Sarah Ripley, Margaret Fuller, Caleb Stetson, Elizabeth Peabody and her brother Ephraim, Emerson and Ripley were among them. Then and there was born the Transcendentalist Club, as it came to be called, although the founders gave it no name; and from that moment Emerson, in spite of his disclaimers and even his very strong distaste, became the leading and shining light round which the increasing crowd of Transcendentalists gathered. His sanity and perfect balance were a striking contrast to the crazier element among those who insisted upon calling themselves his followers; their wild extravagances of thought and act remote from his ordered years as the wisest and tenderest of fathers, the most thoughtful, devoted of husbands, a neighbor always to be counted on, a husbandman careful to develop to the utmost his holdings, the pattern of good citizens in the village he loved. It was his teaching that "there is a correspondence between the human soul and everything that exists in the world," that "a man contains all that is needful for his government within himself," and that "the highest revelation is that God is in every man," that drew them. Here were statements to which the wildest theories could be hung, and many of the conclusions which resulted shocked all Emerson's sound common sense, roused his amusement and affronted the fastidious quality in him which was a powerful element of his character.

In the beginning, however, the new association seemed to promise an aid to the advance of the new thought, and the Sage of Concord gave it as much of his time and his work as was possible. For a while, to be sure, the meetings even of the young men who came to discourse with him, and Lydian's charming teas, were suspended. For on October 30 Lydian bore her husband a son, to whom they gave the name of Waldo.

His working hours over, Emerson delighted to sit beside the great fourposter bed in the westward-looking upper chamber, gazing at the mother and child, in whose tiny person he was obliged to confess that he could not, at first, realize his part. But he thought there could be no more beautiful sight than that of the proud and happy mother and the "*cunning* little nestler" as he called him, the one so full of loving guardianship, the other so little, so helpless.

Emerson was a man of few and rare intimacies. To his own family he gave a deep and entire love; a love that reached its intensest, if different, forms with his brothers Edward and Charles, with Ellen, the unforgotten lost Lenore of his youth, with this little son of his, and with Lydian, the only one among them all he was not to lose to death. He had friends, and dear ones, closest of all being Elizabeth Hoar, almost, he felt, his sister; friends, some of whom, like Dr. Furness of Philadelphia, he had made in boyhood and kept through life. But even these stood outside the innermost circle, and of that circle, past and present, Ellen and Charles, Lydian and little Wallie, as they called him, were the closest and the most precious.

The winter of 1836-37, like its predecessor, was spent in lecturing, both in Boston and near-by towns. His subjects were English Literature, Great Men, the Philosophy of History and allied studies. The admiration for him grew steadily, although in these years it was very largely the same audiences he addressed, the inner, cultured portion of New England society, the students at colleges and professional schools, the reformers who were beginning to center upon him. He was not yet widely known, although all informed thought was aware of him.

Early in February of that season he was asked to deliver an address before the Phi Beta Kappa Society of Harvard. He had announced that his theme would be the appropriate one of "The American Scholar," but somehow there was a strong impression that he would deliver a revolutionary talk. The response was tremendous, as this glimpse given by one among the audience, the eighteen-year-old James Russell Lowell, will show:

"*(It was) without any former parallel in our literary annals, a scene to be always treasured in the memory for its picturesqueness and its inspiration. What crowded and breathless aisles, what windows clustering with eager heads, what enthusiasm of approval, what grim silence of foregone dissent!*"

Emerson appealed to his hearers, who represented to a high degree the trained and thinking men of their different generations, for independence, sincerity, the courage to free themselves from ancient routine, to look for the spirit and not be content with the letter. He spoke with eloquence. He told them that a man trained in books, formed by nature, who developed himself by seeking what was real, what was truth, and who could not be turned away from that seeking by tradition or opinion, was the master of the universe. He was the ideal human being, who had learned complete self-trust, and knew there was no guide greater than his own indwelling spirit. He was heard, as Lowell said, with enthusiasm of approval and with the grim silence of dissent, but no one listened to him unmoved and none could doubt he spoke himself with that sincerity and original thought he demanded.

The dissenting silence became outspoken and loud once those who disapproved were in the open. Emerson remained untroubled. He continued to work out his own philosophy, to seek fresh inspiration in solitude and nature, to read his favorite books, not, as he had by now discovered, for any counsel they gave, but because they stimulated his own thought. And as summer waxed and little Wallie flourished, the meetings at the Emerson house were resumed, the Transcendentalists grew in number, and the eyes of people scattered far and wide began to turn toward Concord, catching a light there that attracted them.

One of the new members of the Club was young Henry David Thoreau, who had been graduated that summer from Harvard and came home to Concord not only with a great admiration for Emerson, but with a sense of gratitude for that friend's help in securing for him the same grant of money from the First Church that had been allowed Emerson when he was an undergraduate. The two families had long been known to each other, the Thoreaus having lived in different houses in or near the village for two generations. Lydian's sister, a widow, Mrs. Lucy Jackson Brown, was boarding with Mrs. Thoreau this summer, in the fine old house at the top of the Square which had been built by grandfather Thoreau, and it was she who brought the shy, uncouth young man to one of the meetings. From then on Henry came pretty constantly; Emerson was interested by the boy's original and independent mind, though he did not care particularly for his poems, which Henry used to toss in to Mrs. Brown as he passed under her window, and which she brought to her brother-in-law. Henry was just twenty, and already master of several languages, completely at ease with Latin, clever with his hands, a true craftsman, familiar also with the natural history of the neighborhood. As a boy of twelve he had helped the great Audubon, recently arrived in America, to collect plant specimens and make notes on birds. Audubon had come from France with letters to the Thoreau family, who were of French descent, and it was through them he met Emerson and began the friendship dear to both. Before leaving college Henry David had written an essay on American literature which was an appeal to American writers to shake off the influence of Europe and produce a native growth. Included was one paragraph that reads as though it might have been written today:

"*Utility is the rallying word with us; we are a nation of speculators, stock brokers and money changers. We do everything by steam because it is more expeditious and cheaper in the long run; we are continually racking our brains to invent a quicker way or quicker method of doing this or that. The question with us is whether a book will take, will sell well; not whether it is* worth *taking or selling.*"

Young Thoreau was one of the few to have read *Nature*, and he had liked that book. He spoke of it to its author with a heartfelt sincerity of admiration that pleased the older man. It made Emerson happy to feel that he gave young men something they wanted, something they could use.

With the coming of the new year Emerson tendered the church at Lexington his resignation, to take effect in February. He had been preaching there for three years and he had reached the point where he never wanted to enter another pulpit. This he confided to his journal in these forthright words:

"I hate preaching, whether in pulpits or in teachers' meetings. Preaching is a pledge, and I want to say what I feel and think today, with the proviso that perhaps tomorrow I shall contradict all. Freedom boundless I wish."

In spite of this step he was asked to speak to the graduating class of ministers on July 15 in the same year, 1838, at the Divinity School of Harvard where he himself had studied. He accepted the invitation with considerable satisfaction. Elizabeth Hoar, when she heard of it, remarked that she wished for once she could have been a divinity student, as she was certain Waldo was going to stir them up as though they'd been a pudding and he the stick, and it was going to be something worth observing. She was right.

When he told the class that what he called historic Christianity had two vital defects, the first of which was its undue dependence on the personal authority of Jesus Christ, the second its entire failure to seek in man's moral nature the real fountain of truth; when, in that matchless voice, he pled with his hearers to seek for redemption in their own souls, to refuse to follow any model, however good, however sanctified in the imagination of men, to cast conformity behind them, and listen only to the voice within, the class would hardly have been surprised to have the roof of the hall fall in on them. To be sure, the Unitarian doctrine denied divinity to Christ, but it allowed him divine authority as directly inspired from God. To be told that each and every man received the same direct inspiration, and that that inspiration alone was to be heeded, was too much. There was a rustle, a murmur at the end, and by the next day controversy flared, the newspapers took it up, and Emerson found himself assailed on every hand. Even by old friends like Dr. Ware. This minister, who had invited Waldo, at the beginning of his career, to follow him as pastor of the Second Church, preached an address the Sunday following that called Emerson gravely to account. Replying to the letter the Doctor sent him, repeating what he had said in the pulpit, Emerson refused to be drawn into a controversy. One paragraph of his answering letter made that clear:

"*I could not possibly give you one of the 'arguments' you covertly hint at on which any doctrine of mine stands. For I do not know what an argument means in reference to an expression of a thought. I delight in telling what I think; but if you ask me, how I dare say so, or why it is, I am the most helpless of men.*"

While the conservatives attacked him, the radicals rushed to his defence. But he himself kept silence, liking his defenders little more than his detractors. "I shall certainly not fall into the vulgar mistake of dreaming that I am persecuted because I am contradicted," he remarked composedly, and returned to his home, his wife, his son and his work in Concord, annoyed only when the papers attempted to invade his privacy to get "his side." He had no side; he had no wish except to say, if he said anything, exactly what he thought.

Not all the ministers were against him, however. Another old friend and distant relative, the Reverend Converse Francis, who came to Concord to see him after the row, as he had often come before, entered these wise sentences into his diary, and perhaps even used them in a sermon:

"Such a calm, steady, simple soul, looking for truth and living in wisdom, in love for man and goodness . . . He is not a philosopher, he is a seer. If you see truth as he does, you will recognize him for a gifted teacher; if not, there is little or nothing to be said . . . But do not brand him with the names of visionary or fanatic or pretender; he is no such thing; he is a true, Godful man, though in his love for the ideal he disregards too much the actual."

The demand for Emerson as a lecturer was not affected by the disapproval of the church men. Rather, it appeared to be stimulated. He was entering the most fertile decade of his life, and rising on the sight of men like a great star in an empty sky.

Chapter XI

Wallie

No portrait of Emerson would be complete that did not tell the story of the vivid child whose

> *"Silver warble wild*
> *Outvalued every pulsing sound*
> *Within the air's cerulean round . . ."*

and whose little feet coming and going on childhood's happy errands were forever bringing good tidings of great joy to his father's heart.

The boy was beautiful, with a heartshaped face and finely modeled head, hair soft, thick and smooth, a broad forehead, dark blue eyes of a notable clearness framed by long curling lashes. His chin was rounded and firm, his mouth full of sweetness, his body vigorous. Above all he had singular charm and not a visitor to the Emerson house, however brief his or her glimpse of Wallie, but remembered him with affectionate pleasure and spoke of him thereafter when there was mention of the home or the family.

Before he was a year old he could be seen tottering along the garden paths, tiny hand clutching one of his father's fingers, stopping to reach for a leaf or a flower or a pebble, sitting suddenly down to smile up at the face bending over him. Presently he was talking, by the time he was two with so clear an enunciation as to make father and mother exchange a delighted smile when some new word was truly spoken. As he grew older he was allowed to play in Emerson's study, the father sitting writing in the chair by the table, the small son on the carpet with his blocks and toys, often odd treasures he picked up and preferred to more conventional playthings. One morning, after he had been taken up for his nap, Lydian came in to ask Emerson some question. There on the floor was a tower the child had built, made of these odds and ends, a cardboard flower box top, a couple of spools, an awl case, cards, bits of wood, all carefully, patiently balanced together. Lydian, laughing, dropped on her knees beside it, kissing it so vigorously that it tumbled down.

"I don't care whether he's asleep or not, I've got to go upstairs and kiss him this minute," she declared. "The darling child!" Smiling, Emerson watched her run off.

The boy never disturbed him. He would murmur away to himself as he played, occasionally putting a question, always gravely answered. He seemed to realize that work was being accomplished that ought not to be interrupted, that in fact the two of them were equally engaged in serious occupation. Now and then, though, he did make an appeal. He had been given a little wooden horse, a spirited creature that had to be tied to prevent its running away. For a while its master toiled in an effort to fasten the reins to a chair leg, then, sighing:

"Please, Papa, will you tie up the horse for me?"

"But I'm writing now, Wallie."

"But my horse *must* be tied up."

"But I *must* write."

Then Waldo brought out his last, his direst threat:

"I will not love you, Papa."

Whereupon, with an inward chuckle but a serious face, Emerson tied up the wild toy horse.

"I *do* love you, Papa!"

A quick, tense child's hug, a kiss, and the writer went back to his essay and the horse trainer to his play.

"Please, Papa, will you tie up the horse for me?"

But it was on their endless jaunts about house and garden when writing was done for the day that the two really conversed. Wallie put endless questions, listened gravely to the answers:

"Papa, what are you putting in the stove?"

"Coal, Wallie."

"Why is this coal so big and this so small?"

"The big is called soft coal, and the small hard coal. They burn well together."

Wallie would nod, his eyes contented.

Or perhaps, little hand in big one, the two stood watching farmer Edmund Hosmer, one of the friends Emerson much admired, dumping sand on the meadow recently acquired:

"Why are they putting all the sand on the grass?"

"So as to fill in the marshy spots. Then you can run all over and pick the daisies and the dandelions without wetting your shoes."

The child was never hushed up, never ignored. Courtesy, Emerson believed, began in the family; was there more needed and more precious than anywhere else. It flowered to its full charm inside the Emerson home, and was as evident in his children as in himself.

The little boy was interested in everything. In the tools in the tool house which he would use with careful absorption if permitted, or watch being used with intense pleasure. Then there were the microscope, the magnet, the small globe of the world in the study, sources of infinite delight. Turning the globe:

"Papa, are there other countries?"

"Yes, many countries besides our own."

"I wish you to name them."

And as his father named them and their cities, he would listen with his air of grave attention that was irresistible. Already at three he was learning his letters from his grandmother, a short lesson each morning, but he learned quickly. He delighted to make up words of his own, and one summer day Margaret Fuller, who had come from Providence on a visit, came in laughing from the garden where she had been helping Mrs. Emerson, to tell Ralph Waldo:

"Waldo's too funny. He's building one of those little houses of his out on the lawn, and when I went to look at it he began naming its parts to me. One was the 'interspeglium,' another the 'coridaga.' And when I asked him why he called his rooms by such strange names, he said 'because the children cannot understand them.'"

For the Emerson house was a haven of delight to the little children of the neighbors who came to play with Wallie and to gaze with delight upon the new baby, born on February 24, 1839, brought out in her little bassinet to enjoy the garden, sitting propped up against a cushion, a dark-eyed little maiden who had been named Ellen. It was Lydian who suggested that name, touching her husband deeply with this proof of her utter lack of jealousy, that whatever was precious to him was precious too to her.

"Lydian," he said, "you make my gods your gods! We will call her Ellen, and you and I will be happier for that name, and the memory it bears of what was beautiful and gentle and good."

After his first view of Ellen he described her in his journal as a "*soft, quiet, swarthy little creature, apparently perfect and healthy . . . Well assured, and very soft and still, the little maiden expresses great contentment with all she finds, and her delicate but fixed determination to stay where she is, and grow.*"

The Emerson place had everything children love, and Wallie knew it all and found a world in it. There was the kennel with the friendly dog; the poultry house and run with exciting chickens; the woodshed from which, when days grew chill, he was allowed to bring in a small log for Grandmama's open fire. There was Dolly, whose nose he could stroke when held up in his father's arms; or, shining with delight, he could sit beside his father in the buggy on village errands or a visit to the Ripleys or the Thoreaus. Dr. Ripley was showing his age but he still came down to sit in the garden or his warm study, and liked to walk slowly down between the ash trees of the driveway with Wallie beside him to bid his little visitor good-bye at the gateway.

But it was Aunt Elizabeth, as he called her, whom he loved most after his father and mother. She had taken him to her heart from earliest babyhood with that "plain, wise love" which Emerson commends in her. She boasted that she "never gave him sugarplums," but she gave him her full attention, she respected as well as loved him, and when she came to the house he would drop his toys or his play with his little mates, and go running to her, sure that the visit was for him.

Like all imaginative children, Wallie's makebelieves were as real to him as the ground under his feet. He was intensely sensitive to beauty, quick to respond to color and to light, quick too to notice what was not attractive and to recoil. One Sunday morning a working neighbor, a stout, kind but unattractive looking woman, dropped into the Emerson kitchen for a word with Louise, the cook, on her way to church. Wallie was there and she asked him to come with her to the church, but he only shook his head shyly.

"Why didn't you want to go with Mrs. Mulford, dear?" asked Louise, when the visitor had left.

"Because Mrs. Mulford isn't beautiful. She has red hands and a red face,"

No more was said, but the following Sunday Wallie asked whether Mrs. Mulford were coming:

"I think it would be nice to go to church with her."

"But I thought you didn't like her," Louise reminded him.

"I made a prayer about her. A little prayer that she might be beautiful and now she seems beautiful."

Toward baby Ellen he adopted a protective attitude that ravished his parents. In the autumn following her birth he began to attend a kindergarten school taught by a Plymouth friend of Lydian's, Mary Russell, lately come to live in Concord. A small group of his playmates went with him, and every morning Emerson used to watch from his study window the setting out of the little cavalcade, with Mary, the housemaid, who also played nurse, pushing the baby carriage containing Ellen, and circling about it the dancing, laughing children. But Wallie walked close beside his sister

> "*With sunny face of sweet repose,*
> *To guard the babe from fancied foes,*
> *The little captain innocent . . .*"

stately in his cap and coat, softly marching "to some tune by fairies played."

No child was ever happier, given a wider range, yet sweetly trained to gentle manners and consideration. In him Emerson lived a double childhood, the boy's and his own lost one that had never been a childhood.

In the spring of 1841 Henry Thoreau came to live with the Emersons. Emerson had considerably increased his land holdings and was setting out an orchard and extending his vegetable garden. He needed help and there was no better gardener in Concord than young Thoreau. But it was more as a service to the young man than to himself that the matter was arranged.

Grief and ill luck had come to the Thoreau family. The school which had been established by Henry's older brother, John, and in which all four of the brothers and sisters taught, opened in 1838 and instantly growing into favor, had had to be closed suddenly in the spring of 1840. John, who was its mainspring, a born teacher and full of original ideas, was laid low with tuberculosis, the old curse of the family which had swept away all the Thoreau uncles in their young manhood. He died in the autumn, but not directly of the disease, though it doubtless influenced the end. A scratch in his finger became infected, lockjaw developed.

Henry adored his brother and the loss was a bitter one. He carried his grief locked up in him, ranging his beloved woods and fields for the only comfort he could find. But when Emerson, of whom he was deeply fond in spite of their temperamental differences, asked him to come to take over his growing orchard and garden, he accepted gladly. The young man delighted in Wallie, the child in him, and both enjoyed long sessions in the woodshed, where Thoreau, deft and skillful with his hands, used to carve charming toys out of wood. One stormy day Henry made a whistle, and as the child blew upon it the sudden thunder rolled. Laughing aloud, Wallie cried, "See, my music makes the thunder dance."

Emerson's unfailing interest in words was caught by many of his children's phrases. "We use ten words to the child's one," he noted, and when Wallie, who had been studying the microscope with minute attention, remarked, "Papa, it hasn't any telling on it," meaning it bore no sterling mark or initials such as his spoon and fork and knife carried, his father was pleased. "It is a better, more direct word than 'name' " he decided; and he was also pleased by Ellen's "Look at the tears on the window, Wallie," during a rainstorm.

And how could he help being interested in Wallie's creative fancy, in the intensity of thought that made thought more real than fact. Wallie, declaring he wanted a bell, went off to find Thoreau and beg him to make him one. So, with stiff paper and paste, a bit of twine, a bit of wood for a clapper, a bell was fashioned which, with a dignified rapture, Wallie brought to Lydian:

"Mamma, may I have this bell we've been making to stand beside my bed?"

"Yes, you may have it to stand there."

At that Wallie looked slightly disturbed:

"But, Mamma, I'm afraid it may alarm you. It may sound in the middle of the night, and it will be heard over the town; it will be louder than ten thousand hawks; it will be heard across the water and in all countries." His eyes shone as the glory of his bell overwhelmed him. "It will sound like some great glass thing which falls down and breaks all to pieces."

But his mother promised, since she would know that it was his bell, not to be alarmed.

The children had their own nursery, and before their bedtime Emerson used to go up for a little visit. One evening Wallie ran to him:

"I want something to play with I never saw before, Papa."

"But why something new? There are the sun and the moon, very old, but good playmates for all that, and as good as new."

"No."

"What do you think of eating and drinking? Rather dangerous toys, perhaps, but don't you think them good amusements, old as they are?"

"Yes, but I want something to play with I never did play with."

"What about water? You play in your bath with water."

Wallie laughed. This game he and his father were playing was new, and he could see in his father's eyes that he thought it a funny game.

One day the circus came to town and Emerson decided to go with his little son. So they went, Wallie sitting gravely on his father's knees, intently observing the trick animals, the tumblers, the trapeze performers like great gay birds flying about in the air. He was far too much surprised at this strange world to make any comment, sitting in a silent attention, an almost disturbed interest. Finally the clown in his immemorial get-up leaped into the ring and began his slapstick tricks, his loud patter. Shouts of laughter greeted him, but Wallie did not laugh. Grasping his father's thumb tightly, he whispered:

"Papa, the funny man makes me want to go home."

"He makes me want to go home too," his father answered, and the two got quietly out of the tent and returned to the house, where Emerson told Lydian, surprised by their early return, what had happened.

"I'm glad," he said, "that our little son was not delighted by the coarse buffoonery, the slapsticking and knockabout of the 'funny man.'"

"So am I," his wife agreed.

As a far jollier way to spend the afternoon Emerson took Wallie down to paddle in the brook, through the flower-filled meadow. A wind blew, and the blossoms swayed to it. Wallie, racing ahead down the narrow path, stopped suddenly, bending down his head, and then, as his father joined him, looking up through his curved lashes with laughing eyes:

"The flowers talk when the wind blows them, Papa."

"So they do."

Content in each other, the two went on together.

That September, 1841, Dr. Ripley died; that last, as Emerson wrote, of those "great, grim, earnest men, the Puritans." They had built New England, raised her "unpainted churches, with their strict platforms and sad offices, and the wearisome prayers rich with the diction of ages." Their time had passed, yet they took away with them something great and fine.

In the spring of this year Emerson had definitely refused to join the Brook Farm experiment. He had far too sound an appreciation of what he, at least, required in life to lend himself to this Utopian scheme. He disliked and distrusted the urge to do things in groups; could not be convinced that a number of extremely dissimilar persons, even though inspired by a like impulse, would do better living in a forced intimacy than by pursuing their separate ways. With a touch of humor he made his apology in these words:

"I stay where I am, even with the degradation of owning bank stock and seeing poor men suffer while the universal genius apprises me of this disgrace, and beckons me to the martyr's and redeemer's office . . . This staying by our work is belief too."

He wrote Carlyle that he had food, shelter, warmth, a kitchen garden, a flower garden; that he had planted an orchard of young trees; that he enjoyed an income of six per cent amounting to about a thousand two hundred dollars; that his lectures brought in from eight hundred to a thousand a year; that his wife was the incarnation of Christianity, his mother the whitest, mildest, most conservative of old ladies, his son a piece of love and sunshine. He added that he had three domestics and that he spent his time reading and writing, but with very little system. He allowed his friend to infer that he was a happy man.

On November 22, 1841, his third child, Edith was born; a tiny weazened baby but perfectly healthy, who looked, her father said, amused, to his wife, to be "of an incredible age." But she soon began to look younger and by Christmas was quite presentable. There was a little party to celebrate the day at the Emersons' to which Wallie's and Ellen's little friends were invited, with a delicious tea and gifts for everyone, and plenty of games and a world of laughter.

The day after Christmas a neighbor told them that scarlet fever had broken out in the village. It was before the era of strict quarantine, but the Emersons kept their children at home and evaded outside contact themselves so far as possible.

But on January 22 Waldo came down with a sore throat and fever. Dr. Bartlett, hastily summoned, found he had caught the disease. All the proper precautions were taken, and for the first two days the child seemed but lightly attacked. He even dictated a letter to his cousin William, William's eldest son, who had sent him a magic lantern, in which he said:

"*I wish you would tell cousin Willie that I have so many presents that I do not need that he should send me any more unless he wishes to very much.*"

But suddenly there was a turn for the worse.

On January 28 Emerson set down one line in his journal:

"*Yesterday night, at fifteen minutes after eight, my little Waldo ended his life.*"

The terrible suddenness of the calamity stunned the father, and after the first frantic reaction to his grief he fell into silence and a kind of apathy that frightened him. He wrote his friend Dr. Furness that "I do not want to mourn the innocent and beautiful sourly and gloomily, but with music and fragrant thoughts and sportive recollections." But oh, it seemed to him that his child had been "too precious and unique a creation to be huddled aside into the waste and prodigality of things."

Thoreau wrote to Lydian's sister, who had returned to Plymouth, that Waldo had died "*as the mist rises from the brook, which the sun will soon dart his rays through. Do not the flowers die every autumn? He had not even taken root here. I was not startled to hear that he was dead; it seemed the most natural death that could happen. His fine organization demanded it, and Nature gently yielded its request.*"

But his son's death did not appear natural to Emerson. Returning home after filling a lecture engagement in Providence a month later, he writes:

"*Home again from Providence. Dear friends find I, but the wonderful boy is gone,*" and he notes hearing little Ellen ask her grandmother, "*Can't God stay alone a little while with the angels and let Waldo come back,*" adding: "*What a looking for miracles have I. As his walking into the room where we are would not surprise Ellen, so it would seem to me the most natural thing in the world.*"

In the poem *Threnody*, with its heartbreaking beauty, written though it was after time had done its blessed work of healing, we may read something of what Emerson's son meant to him, of his grief, and of the acceptance of that grief as part of the great experience of living. His life was immensely greater and deeper because of the child whom he had loved, and that child had gone out of the world unshadowed during all his five radiant years. He would, indeed, not sourly mourn him, but remember him with music and with fragrant thought.

CHAPTER XII

The Twelve Full Years

THE period stretching between the year 1835 and the end of the year 1847 when Emerson made his second trip to England, was rich in accomplishment and in experience. His four children, Wallie, Ellen, Edith and Edward were born to him, and Wallie was taken away, developing the deepest emotions of fatherhood, while intellectually he reached the fulness of his philosophy, gave it a marvellous expression in series after series of lectures, and published two volumes of *Essays*, the first in 1841, the second in 1844, following these with the *Poems* in 1846. He reached through these years complete maturity, a maturity like that of a noble tree, which continues to flourish and to yield its fruit decade after decade, blessing the world in which it exists.

His great fame as lecturer was built up during these years. Yet he did not want to lecture. More than most men he disliked separating himself from his home and his family, and no place on earth was dear to him as were Boston and Concord. A good neighbor, he attended Town Meeting and was on the school board. He kept open house, and he called on his friends, coming, as Hawthorne said, with "a sunbeam in his face." He delighted in his peaceful mornings of work, in the rambles through fields and woods and to the hill-tops, usually solitary, occasionally with Thoreau or Ellery Channing as companion, except on Sundays, when three or four of his friends might make up a party; but on those occasions there was apt to be more talk than walk. Emerson did his thinking outdoors, caught there his inspirations, and for this preferred to be alone.

But money was necessary. His writings brought him little for many years, his small income, even with Lydian's to help, was not enough for what both wanted in life. Not luxury, but charm and serenity of living, an attractive home though a simple one. The children must be considered, given schooling, be sweetly cared for. Lydian was not strong and needed servants she could trust. Beyond these personal requirements Emerson was forever helping out friends in need, and besides friends, utter strangers who appealed to him for no better reason than that they knew his name.

It was he who introduced Carlyle to America, not only in the introduction to the American edition of his friend's first book, *Sartor Resartus*, but by guaranteeing the publisher against loss and shouldering some of the expense of printing; a bill for paper alone costing him five hundred dollars. It was several years before Carlyle's growing reputation increased the demand for that and succeeding books, also sponsored by Emerson, so reimbursing him for his outlay in their behalf, an expense he had taken care to keep from Carlyle. This is only one example of his generosity. Another is his paying the rent for a year of the cottage to which the Alcotts came, after Bronson's school in Boston had blown up, leaving the family practically destitute. More than this, Louisa has told us how, after any one of his visits, they would find a five or ten dollar bill tucked under a book on the table, and what godsends such offerings were.

So winter after winter, spring after spring, Emerson gave his lecture series in Boston and neighboring towns, going as far afield as New York, Baltimore, Philadelphia, Newport on his rounds. These lectures were built up out of his notebooks and from lectures and notebooks together the essays grew in their turn. A slow writer, he spent that part of the year not lecturing in working over his material, reducing, as he put it, "my formless scriptures into shape."

What he spoke, what he wrote were variations on a single theme, but that theme was infinite. It was the divinity of the individual. That was the foundation rock on which he built. Illuminating his theme was his invincible optimism, which he defines in a single sentence:

"The genius which preserves and guides the human race indicates itself by a small excess of good, a small balance of brute fact always favorable to the side of reason."

Such a balance, however small, is enough, in the long reach of time, to evolve the angel from the brute, and Emerson was on the side of the angel.

He had, as we have seen, been hailed as the leader of transcendentalism. What was this philosophy, if it were one?

In his first book, *Nature*, Emerson wrote on "the feeling of the infinite." This feeling was the basis of transcendentalism, and he elaborated upon it from that time on. Always rebelling against exact definitions, he insisted that truth must be grasped intuitively; that the transcendental perception was its own answer, needing no proof.

Amplifying on his conception somewhat he suggests that Reason is of the same essence as God. Reason in man is divinity, it is above time and space, it is absolute truth. Opposed to this divine essence is the world of Nature, the material world in which we live and to which our own material part belongs, created by the Divine Mind as the ultimate effect of Itself, the Cause. Between these two is man's Understanding, the handmaid, the working human element of this God-Reason within. From Reason Understanding draws all it needs to build perfection. And since the material world is only the effect of Reason, of Divine Mind, then a man, choosing to draw from that source existing within him, flowing constantly into him from God Himself, can make his outward life and the outward world according to that pattern. "Build," cried Emerson, "your own world. As fast as you conform your life to the pure idea in your mind, that will unfold its grand proportions."

So far so good. But an effect of this declaration was to induce a great many persons who believed they had hold of this central force to insist that their ideas of the world and of man, being necessarily true, since they had been drawn from the Reason within, should be adopted. And if they were not adopted, then the thing to do was to get as far as possible from things as they were. The average ideas were wrong, so naturally the average behavior was wrong. The wilder enthusiasts therefore set up all manner of Reforms, joined themselves into little bands who refused this or that result of civilization, sometimes meat, sometimes living in houses, so that they went back to caves, sometimes this or the other practice. There must be no compromise involving any let-down of their high ideal, no disobedience to the dictates of that inner Reason. With a feeling of conscious right these frantic souls denied themselves the comforts, the companionships, the delights of human existence, rebuking by their stand the faults of society.

It was these people who gave transcendentalism its black eye with the ordinary citizen, and evoked the flood of ridicule under which it was finally swamped. But these exaggerations were entirely foreign to Emerson. They annoyed or amused him as the case might be. He found no fault with the fine results of man's long progress from barbarism to civilization, any more than with the beauty of a rose or the song of a bird. They were to be accepted with pleasure and with thanks. But he wanted men, as he said, who were "drenched in Time, to come out of Time and taste their native, immortal air . . . find the ideal and holy life, the forgotten Good . . ." He wanted them to turn from absorption in the material interests of existence to recognition of their immortal quality, to remember that they were linked to God as well as to Nature.

On this theme then he talked, and though many in his audiences were puzzled, all were enthralled. Longfellow declared Waldo to be the finest lecturer he had ever heard, with magnificent passages of true prose-poetry, and never missed hearing him when he lectured in Boston, although asserting that what he spoke was "all dreamery, after all." Indeed it became inconceivable in Boston for any cultivated man or woman to stay away from his series. But these people were not his entire audience. The plain citizen, the simple and the ordinary men and women of that and other places, delighted in him. It was the man himself they liked to listen to; the man who turned dust to flame for them; who made them believe, without their quite understanding how he did it, that you were capable of magnificence, that you shared existence with the shining ones, were of their company.

The newspapers spread Emerson's fame until it echoed all over the America of that day. Even as far afield as the wilderness towns in Ohio, Illinois, Indiana his name became known and people desired to hear him. After his return from England he thus extended his journeys to the very frontier, meeting the hardships involved without pleasure but stoically, and speaking in dreary, chill halls to puzzled yet attracted gatherings with an amused comprehension that many among them understood nothing he was trying to expound, that he was merely an "entertainment," that filled an otherwise empty evening.

It was the great era of lectures, begun by a certain Josiah Holbrook, a good natural talker and something of a scientist, who conceived the notion of going about through New England giving free lectures on geology, physical geography and natural history. At the end of his talks he would ask for questions, and finish up with a plea that the town or village where he was speaking would inaugurate a library and free debating societies, to which he gave the name of Lyceum, from the Greek. His idea took hold and presently spread like wildfire. Concord, soon after Holbrook had visited the place, opened its own Lyceum, destined to become the best known in the land. The first lecture given for it, in the old brick schoolhouse on the Square near the Thoreau home, was by Waldo's brother Edward, the first of a long line of distinguished men to speak under its auspices, among whom were Alcott, Wendell Phillips, Thoreau, James Freeman Clarke, Theodore Parker, Agassiz, Longfellow, Horace Greeley, even John Brown, brought there by Thoreau. Emerson of course spoke there many times. The meetings after a while were held in the vestry of the Unitarian church, and when this proved too small a place, in a room in the Town Hall.

Another interest, and allied to the transcendental cause, was the *Dial*, which was started as a publication where free discussion of all the revolutionary ideas and schemes abroad could be secured. Emerson had no very strong hope that the *Dial* could become really important, nor even that it could last long. But he gave his time and help to it, first while Margaret Fuller was its editor and when she resigned in 1843, editing it himself. In its first number he explained the aims of the little magazine in an eloquent foreword, saying that it proposed to be the voice for those revolutionaries who were to be found everywhere, but who "have no external organization, no badge, no creed, no name . . . united only in a common love of truth and love of its work. They are of all conditions and constitutions . . . trudging beside teams in dusty roads, drudging as hirelings in other men's fields, schoolmasters who teach a few children for a pittance, ministers of small parishes in the obscurer sects, lone women in dependent conditions, matrons and young women, beautiful and hard-favored, (who) have silently given their adherence to a new hope . . . a greater trust in the nature and resources of man than the law or the popular opinion of man will well allow."

It spoke, in fact, for the New Deal of that day, and its contributors ranged from sound and sane men, like Emerson himself, down to wildest visionaries beside whom Alcott or Thoreau were mild indeed. Emerson, writing at that time to Carlyle, admitted as much, saying "we are all a little wild here, with numerous projects of social reform . . . I am gently mad myself." But he maligned himself.

Not but what he tried out an occasional reform, and Lydian, laughing, told Elizabeth Hoar that she used to run into the kitchen and fling a new plan at her cook much as a small boy might throw a stone through a window and then race off. One time it was meat that came under the ban, but not for long. Finding no benefit from the denial, Waldo, with a little smile, suggested that they might as well patronize the butcher, a good man, again. Another time, after a discussion with a few friends regarding the essential equality of people, he asked Lydian if she did not agree with him that it was but right to invite the three domestics to eat their meals with the family. Lydian, who never opposed him, though somewhat dismayed as she realized the inconveniences of this new idea, agreed to ask the servants how they would like it. They didn't like it a bit. As cook said, they enjoyed having their meals to themselves, talking of what pleased them.

"I quite understand," Lydian agreed, "and I'm sure I feel exactly the same myself."

There was, certainly, nothing of the confirmed faddist in Ralph Waldo Emerson.

It was in 1841 that Thoreau joined the Emerson household, partly to keep an eye over Emerson's garden and orchard, partly as secretary. Since the school run by the brothers had failed, and since his brother's death, Henry had been at a loose end. Emerson's unfailingly kind perception saw that the young man needed a fresh incentive. The plan appeared excellent for both. Unluckily Thoreau was not a man who could adapt himself to others; he was in fact rather proud of not doing so, impatient of a viewpoint not his own, argumentative, difficult. The gentle courtesy of the Emerson household irked him, seemed to him trivial. You ought to speak out whatever you thought whether it hurt or not, you ought to contradict flatly, you ought to be yourself without consideration of anyone else. He went about with a chip on his shoulder and wearied Emerson with a roughness and an uncouthness hard to endure. As Elizabeth Hoar had said, you could love Thoreau but you could not like him, and it is necessary to like a person who lives in the same house with you.

Thoreau remained in the Emerson house for a year after Wallie's death, but by then both men knew a change would be better. Emerson thought he had found a fortunate way out of the situation when his brother William, with whom he was staying while giving a series of lectures in New York, asked if he could recommend some young man as tutor for his eldest boy.

Thoreau had proved himself a good teacher, and Emerson's children were all fond of him. Since the Judge, for William was now a Judge, had moved to Staten Island, to a fine, comfortable house close to the sea, Thoreau could continue those studies of nature and wood tramps he loved, and he would have considerable time to himself for his writing, in which he was becoming interested. Both William and Susan, his wife, were sedate, warm-hearted persons, easy to get on with.

"I think it might be an excellent plan. Young Thoreau is of

a somewhat difficult temperament, but honest and honorable as man can be. He has an unusual intelligence. If you can keep from arguing with him you are safe, William."

William smiled. "I'm a lawyer, Waldo. But I think I can promise to leave the young man to his own opinions."

The matter was settled when Emerson returned to Concord and in May, 1843, Henry left for his new position with a good deal of interest. He had had a glimpse of New York on a business trip when he was nineteen, and he felt that he would enjoy knowing it better. He had met William once or twice, casually, and liked what he remembered of him.

The Hawthornes had come to live in Concord during the summer of 1842, taking the Old Manse, which had stood empty since the old Doctor's death. They had only just been married, and had been attracted to Concord by the fact that Emerson lived there. Thoreau had helped to put the garden of the Manse in order, even as another friend of Sophia, Elizabeth Hoar, saw to the work done inside the house in repairing and redecorating. Henry was the young couple's first guest at dinner, and he at once interested Hawthorne, who had not before met him. But after the young man had gone Hawthorne told Sophia that he could not see Thoreau and Emerson as housemates. It appeared to him an impossible combination.

"It is only Waldo who makes it possible," Sophia answered. "Yet it is he who must suffer most against the pricks and knots of this young man." Yet they agreed that Thoreau had possibilities of greatness that promised value for the future.

Within nine months of his departure Thoreau was back in Concord. He had found the Staten Island house and family absolutely incompatible. There was too much wealth, there was an entirely different acceptance of the values of life, possibly a slight stodginess that oppressed him. After the high thinking and plain living, a plainness far removed from bareness or lack of beauty though it was, to which he had been used at the Emerson place in Concord, he was unhappy in this new environment. He grew sarcastic, and some of this sarcasm he vented on the children, who, after the enchantment of Wallie, seemed dull to him. He was not liked, and the best thing was to cut the situation short.

For a year he floated about in Concord, working at odd jobs and meditating an idea that had long possessed him. With the coming of the next spring, in 1845, he set about turning this idea into reality.

He would live entirely by himself, in a house of his own building, a cabin in which he would have nothing but what was necessary to him, made by his own hands. He would raise what food he ate, with something over to buy the few additional items he cared for. He would be independent, master of his time, and he would learn what he wanted to do and to be, have time to think what life meant to him.

The site where his cabin should stand was on the edge of Walden Pond, on land belonging to Emerson. With an axe borrowed from Alcott, Henry felled the pines required for the framework of his home, which was to consist of a room ten by fifteen feet, an attic and a cellar. Deserted shacks along the railway where the workers had lived while the line was under canstruction provided planks for the roof and the sides, frames for the two windows and the door. It was not the first time Henry had built, for with his father and brother he had helped to erect the "hand-made" house on the lane beyond the railway to which the family moved after the school was given up, and which was nicknamed the Texas House because it was so far south of the village proper. He had no difficulty in digging and lining the cellar with stones selected from the fields, and friends dropped over to help him raise the timbers. Begun in April, the cabin was ready, walls plastered, fireplace built, and a hand-made table, chair, and bed, by July Fourth, when Henry moved in.

Concord was excited. People did not camp out in those days, and since he had a perfectly good home with his people the whole notion seemed crazy. What on earth could he do with himself, off there alone in the woods, month after month? Cooking his own grub, and for that grub being satisfied with a porridge of grain, berries, apples, a rasher of bacon. Mad, that was what was the matter with Thoreau!

Yet he was only two miles from the heart of Concord, in a well-built, comfortable shack, able to get home easily. He did so often, occasionally spending a night, often sharing a meal. Visitors came to see him, sat under the pines with him, shared his boiled rye and baked potatoes, after his field began to yield. He had prepared a piece of ground near by which had been cleared and left rough, and which also belonged to Emerson, planting the usual vegetables, including a big patch of corn.

For a few months over two years Thoreau lived at Walden Pond, winter and summer. He divided his time to suit himself, working in his vegetable patch, cutting firewood, swimming in the clear water, writing at his table with door and windows wide, when weather was fine, snug with his roaring fire when the cold came. His first book, *A Week on the Concord and Merrimac Rivers*, was written there. He had been able to study natural history as it was found in the country round about him at his ease, with leisure and at all hours and seasons. He had gathered the material for what was to be his best book, *Walden*. When he concluded to end the experiment he said he had got what he wanted out of it. He had not intended to be a hermit, nor was he one, but he did wish for entire independence, independence from other people's rules and hours, from home chatter, from conformity. He found all these, and he discovered that he was perfectly able to supply his own needs so far as his physical existence went. Why keep on? He decided to come back to village life at the end of the summer of 1847.

Meanwhile Emerson had gone on with his own work. His three books were received with high praise both in his own land, and in England, where Carlyle, delighted to have the chance, introduced them, as Emerson had introduced his, though a guarantee was not demanded by the English publishers. It was long, however, before any appreciable income came to the author, many years before his contracts were put on a proper business basis. Only on his lecture tours could he depend for a real monetary return.

After Wallie's death the desolate man had worked harder than before. Work was an anodyne as well as a necessity. But the inward wound continued to bleed. Lydian, ever alert to his well-being, saw that as time passed a growing lassitude burdened him. He was happy with her and with his three children, delighting in little Nell's blossoming mind as she developed, in the younger children's baby sweetness. But there seemed to be a spring broken that time did not mend.

She wished he might have a complete change, see new faces, new places, lead life to a new rhythm. And fortunately her wish was realized.

England, interested in his books, awake to his fame in America as a speaker, longed to hear him. His friends there wrote him, urging a lecture tour of several months, promising him good fees, telling him they needed to have him once more within touch. In the winter of 1846 these suggestions became concrete, a definite tour was planned, arrangements for it outlined. He must come!

Lydian added her voice to England's.

"But I don't want to leave you here alone, without a man in the house," he told her, toward May, when the plans were really forming.

She saw that he meant it. He would be too worried to enjoy the trip. She was frail in health, winter was a difficult season. His own trips away were for short periods, he was always coming and going. But eight or ten months . . .

Lydian decided that a way out of this impasse must be found. By now the Hawthornes had left and Emerson's uncle, the Reverend Samuel Ripley, with his wife, Sarah, that remarkable union of a perfect domestic character, abounding humor, delightful hospitality and extraordinary learning, were living at the Old Manse, which had descended to Samuel. There was no better counsellor than Sarah, and Lydian went to her with her problem.

"Ask Henry Thoreau. You can get on with him perfectly, the children like him, he is as practical as he is queer, you couldn't have a better man about the house. And I happen to know that he's coming out of his hole in the woods with the end of this summer."

The problem was solved. Henry accepted, Emerson felt entirely safe in leaving his wife, his mother and his children in his friend's care, and the tour abroad was decided upon. The rest of the summer and early fall Waldo gave to preparing the lectures he was to give through England. On October 5 Thoreau saw him off from Boston and returned to the white house on Lexington Road with great content. The children welcomed him with joy, dragged him out to play. A few months later in a letter to Emerson, Thoreau, giving the news of the family, added:

"Lydian and I make very good housekeepers. She is a very dear sister to me. . . Eddie very seriously asked me the other

day, 'Mr. Thoreau, will you be my father?' I am occasionally Mr. Rough-and-Tumble with him that I may not miss him, *and lest he should miss* you *too much. So you must come back soon, or you will be superseded."*

Chapter XIII

England Revisited

Alexander Ireland, the youthful Scot who had been the first to welcome Emerson to Edinburgh fourteen years before, was on the pier at Liverpool to greet his friend on this second visit to the British Isles. Alexander had been foremost in arranging the lecture tour that was to begin on October 30. It was a stiff schedule, with a lecture every evening for the first three weeks, divided between Liverpool and Manchester. But there was nearly a week of leisure until the start.

"Here's a letter from Carlyle, Mr. Emerson, that was to be put into your hands the moment you set foot on English soil," and Ireland handed him an envelope. "He's wanting to see you, the sooner the better, I know, and when you get settled at the hotel where there's a room waiting for you I'd advise your going up to London. You'll need a bit of rest first, though. What was the voyage like?"

"Any sea voyage is a dreadful thing, Ireland. Thank God, it's over! Let's see, this is Saturday. I'll take the train on Monday"–he glanced through Carlyle's note–"he asks me to stay with him for as long as I can. I can give him two days safely?"

"That'll allow you a day of rest here before you begin the course. Will that be enough?"

Emerson thought it would, and on Monday Ireland saw him off for London. The railway had reached Concord in 1844, so that by now Emerson was well used to traveling by rail;

It was Jane who threw it open, with Thomas behind her, a lamp in his hands

but the English train proved a new experience. A little later, when he had done a good deal of traveling through the island, he wrote to Lydian in high praise, telling her "I ride everywhere as on a cannon ball (though cushioned and comforted in every manner) high and low, over rivers and towns, through mountains in tunnels of three miles and more, at twice the speed and with half the motion of our cars."

Jane and Thomas Carlyle were both waiting to greet him when at ten that night he knocked at the pretty door of the little house in Cheyne Row. It was Jane who threw it open, with Thomas behind her, a lamp in his hands, his shaggy head bent forward, in his eyes a look of pleasure and affection.

"Well, here we are, shovelled together again," he exclaimed, and handing the lamp to Jane, he grasped both of his friend's hands in his. In spite of the fact that they had seen each other only once before, during the long-ago visit Emerson had spent at Craigenputtock, so intimate and constant had been their correspondence that both felt as though the other were a lifelong friend.

Jane had a little cold supper waiting, which she shared with them, brewing a pot of tea to go with it, and then leaving them to mount to the study at the top of the house. There, Carlyle with his pipe, Emerson with a cigar, the two men talked until the small hours. Or rather, Carlyle talked and Emerson listened, truly astounded at the vigor and range of the Scot's opinions. Germany, France, England, leaped into focus. Great men of the day, literary, scientific, political, took their turn for a thumping. Nothing was right and no one worth his salt. Parliament, a babble of windbags! Darwin, Milnes, Gladstone, may God defend me from sympathizing with their sort! All that Emerson, thoroughly amused, delighted with the flash and sparkle and interested in the fiery judgments of his host, needed to do was to ask a question, mention a name.

"But," protested the American gently, when Thomas paused for breath and, as it were, to gaze round upon the havoc he had wrought, "surely the world is treating you well, Carlyle. You've a host of friends, and people run to buy your books and to hear your lectures."

"Yes, yes! They come to listen to me, and they read what I write. But is there one among them has the smallest intention of doing what I bid them? Not one! No, they're all conspiring to bring the world to ruin, and it's only because they've not the brains to carry out what they wish that has saved us so far."

And Carlyle, as was apt to be his way at the end of one of his tirades, catching the smile on Waldo's face, threw back his head with a great shout of laughter.

"Well, now I've finished damning the world, maybe we'd better be off to our beds. Our dreams'll be all the sweeter, I'm thinking," he said.

For the next two days Emerson saw London under Carlyle's guidance. The historian Bancroft was in London, with his wife, and with them the two companions took tea the first afternoon, meeting the famous collector, Samuel Rogers, whose ten o'clock breakfasts were a London institution. Rogers lived in a superb house packed with treasures, and there was no man or woman of note who had come to London for the past fifty years who had not been a guest at one of these breakfasts. He asked Emerson to come next day with the Bancrofts who were already promised.

This was the first of many occasions when the tall, quiet New Englander, with his austere charm, his courtesy that mingled quaintness, kindness and breeding with a genuine interest in whomever he encountered, was to meet the very best of London society in the interlocking worlds of literature, science and politics. Before he returned to America he had been introduced to the Prince Consort, the amiable Albert; had lunched with the Duchess of Sutherland at Stafford House, finest of English palaces, one of the noblest houses in the world; had been an honored guest at great functions, at smaller, private gatherings of the greatest distinction. He found the simplicity, the genuineness of these aristocrats the most comfortable social atmosphere imaginable, and wrote his wife that he "would gladly forget that there was anything else in England than these golden chambers and the gentle people who walk in them." But he warned her that she must not expect all this hobnobbing with the great to have made any change in him. He assured her that his rough country manners and chill social attitude had not mellowed. She smiled over that, thoroughly aware of her husband's patrician bearing, his unconscious graciousness.

During his lecture tour, which covered all central England, Emerson for the first time gave up his custom of stopping at hotels, and accepted the invitations that came to him to be the guest of one or another of the leading men in the different towns he visited. Most of his hosts were of course entire strangers to him, but again and again he witnesses to the friendliness, the whole-heartedness of his welcome. In his almost daily correspondence home, for he would carry on a letter from one sailing to another, he repeats to Lydian that the English were the most courteous and considerate of people. What was more, he declared that to have their respect you must speak your mind to them; that they "didn't expect the traveler to sneak about diffidently, but to make up his mind and carry his points."

The picturesque details of English life caught his interest, the horses and dogs that went about in the raw weather "entirely clothed," the dog-drawn little carts delivering milk, the sedan chairs still in use here and there. Above all the robustness of the people struck him. "An American feels like an invalid in their company." He spoke too of the Englishman's love for his country which translated itself into good citizenship. "There is no other country with so many good citizens," he noted in his diary.

But each large town, at least, had its dreadful evidences of a poverty far more extreme than anything America knew, and this distressed him. This was what he wished he could forget when in those "golden chambers" of the upper class. In particular it was the destitute, ragged children who made his heart ache. Little girls standing in the wet cold hoping for the gift of a ha'penny, little girls no older than his own small Edith. Thinking of her he could never refuse an alms, and his eyes would dwell on the thin, pale faces with a look of infinite pity.

His lectures were received with acclaim, and reported at length in the papers, this against his will. Since many were repeated in different cities he felt that they lost freshness and interest through having been thus summarized. But England took him to its heart, and here again, as at home, it was the young especially who crowded to listen to him. "I fear that I have beguiled them here, as I have at home, with some better hope than I can realize for them," he wrote. No one had spoken as he spoke to these young men and women, no one seemed so confident of the worth of life, of that "better hope." Often too, here as at home, it was not what he said, it was the man himself who mattered. Crabbe Robinson, famous war correspondent, journalist, barrister diarist, who had been the intimate friend of Charles Lamb, wrote a friend that he had gone to a reception at Lord Northampton's merely out of curiosity to see Emerson, who was to be there. "I had disliked everything of his I had read," Robinson reported, "but in an instant, when I saw him, my dislike vanished. He has one of the most interesting countenances I ever beheld – a combination of intelligence and sweetness that quite disarmed me."

When Emerson met Tennyson he was reminded, somewhat oddly, of Hawthorne. "Take away Hawthorne's shyness, and have him talk easily and fast, and you would have a pretty good Tennyson," he writes. Carlyle had told him that there was no better man in London to smoke a pipe with, and Emerson agreed that the poet was an excellent companion. The encounter took place shortly before the American was to leave England for a brief visit to France, while Tennyson was going to Italy. It was May, 1848, with the French in one of their periodical revolutions.

"You come to Italy with me," Tennyson urged. "You'll only get hit by a flying bullet in that mad Paris. I've been trying to induce Carlyle to come to Rome with me in vain; if I can hold you out as bait, the three of us can make a jaunt of it."

It was tempting, but Emerson's plans were definitely made and not to be changed. In his turn he tried to persuade Tennyson to alter his design, but Alfred had no fondness for the French capital. So the two parted to see each other no more.

Before this meeting Emerson had gone north to Edinburgh with Ireland, to see a few of the old friends who remained there, and to make new ones. Chief among these was De Quincey, who had been rescued from utter penury and cured of the opium habit by staunch friends, and was now living some distance out of town in a tiny cottage with his two daughters. The gentle old man attracted Emerson extremely at the first meeting, which was at a small dinner given for a few literary folk, including the famous Christopher North, who lectured at the University under his own name, Wilson. Emerson did not care for Wilson, and had found his lecture at the University a "dull, rambling affair," containing nothing of the value shown in his writings. De Quincey, utterly different as he and Emerson were in almost everything else, yet had a fundamental likeness to him in what Lowell called "the grace of perfect breeding, everywhere persuasive and nowhere emphatic;" and in a shyness that was never rude, and that included a faculty for being completely at ease with people of any rank, high or low. De Quincey was one of the most exquisite of conversationalists, his English a silver flow of perfectly chosen words, his thought moving with freedom and breadth. In Emerson this small, fragile man, with his beautiful head, his almost feminine features, his extreme sensitiveness, felt the tie of what was alike in both. He asked Emerson to come to his own house for dinner before leaving the city; Waldo accepted and counted the evening spent in the plain little cottage, over the simple meal, alone with De Quincey and his delightful daughters, as one of the precious memories of that year.

While still in Edinburgh a letter from Lydian told of the death of Uncle Samuel. As we have seen, he and his wife Sarah had returned to the Old Manse, which had been reluctantly given up to them by the Hawthornes, as Nathaniel has told in his *Mosses.* The Ripleys yearned to be back in their old home, however, for Samuel had given up the ministry, needing rest. But now that rest was profound. Sarah remained, that wise and witty woman whom Emerson greatly admired, and he wrote back to Lydian to be sure to see as much of the widow as was possible.

So successful had the lectures been that Emerson was being urged to give them in London. But he refused to repeat what he felt had become outworn. He could not bring any freshness to talks that every London paper had quoted and discussed, and when his friends told him that it was himself rather than what he said that people wanted, he was annoyed.

He had, however, been greatly interested in the expositions of physical science in clear and attractive terms, being given by Owen and Faraday, both of whom he had met. He had enjoyed talking with these two scientists, listening to Faraday describe his experiments with electricity, to Sir Richard Owen relating the mysteries of fossil life. He began to think it might be possible to reduce the laws of the powers and functions of the mind to scientific terms, attractively stated. And when it became evident that his refusal to lecture in London was going to disappoint a great many people, among them some very dear friends, he decided that he would give a course based on this idea and to be called "The Natural History of the Intelligence."

He must prepare this course, so he settled in comfortable lodgings in town and for the next six weeks gave each morning to writing, spending the latter part of the day and evening with his friends or as guest at the houses of the great. There was probably not a person worth meeting in London with whom he had not had at least a passing contact. On his way back from Edinburgh he had stopped off at Ambleside, in the Lake country, to see Harriet Martineau, one of the first of women writers for children; an original and forceful woman whose life had been a series of tragedies, but who had allowed neither her grief nor her very delicate health to warp her spirit. She had visited Boston in 1834 and advocated abolition with a great fervor, which brought her a storm of adverse criticism; but Emerson had liked her at once. He liked her now even more, in her little home, The Knoll. Her book on *Household Education*, advocating freedom and rationality as against command and obedience in the training of the young, was then on the press, and she was full of it. Emerson's own ideas were largely in sympathy with this theory, but perhaps not so much with her devotion to mesmerism as a healing power. She was convinced that her own recovered health was entirely due to mesmeric treatments, and eager that others should discover its benefits. Walking together over her little farm, where she not only employed needy villagers in the work required, but gave them the resulting produce for their families, the two discussed these and other subjects with a delightful informality. Perhaps it was the homely charm of this visit that helped to make the later call on Wordsworth unsatisfactory. Emerson liked him even less than on the earlier visit; found him bitter, railing against all Scots, with Carlyle, whom he called a "pest" at their head, reciting his own poems in a stentorian singsong, keeping his genius out of sight.

It was after finishing the writing of his lectures that his trip to Paris was due, the trip Tennyson had tried to persuade him from taking. It was May, the most magical month in the French capital. Arthur Hugh Clough, the English poet, part of whose boyhood had been spent in America, had just resigned from his tutorship at Oxford, and was to be Emerson's companion on the trip. Before they left Clough took Emerson to Oxford, where he introduced to him a small group among his erstwhile students of whom he was particularly proud. Chief among these were Palgrave, of *The Golden Treasury* still far in the future, and Froude, with all his histories still to write. Emerson was more delighted with this visit, with these "noble youths," as he termed them, with the Oxford scene and the charm and friendliness of students and professors than with any other single experience in Britain. Needless to say that the youths in question delighted in him. Clough had brought him down at their urgent demand, and the two days of his stay among them remained golden in the memory of all. Emerson wrote home that these young men had shown him not only the kindest attention, "but more, much more, they had shown me themselves."

From his pension in the Rue des Petits Augustins, in the very heart of Paris, Emerson watched the alarums of the small revolution that was gathering force. But he did not remain within doors. Out he went, saw the wild charges of cavalry through the streets; cannon being dragged from one place to another; the immense display of arms on the boulevards and in the squares, with the sound of the trumpets high above the clamor; mingled with the vast crowds that milled about, crowding to snatch the handbills hot from the presses being issued by either side or to listen as they were read aloud by the messengers, or to read the proclamations that succeeded each other on the walls, one pasted above another. Over the Palace of the Tuileries he looked up at the tri-couleur proudly floating, proof that the Socialist Party had not yet won. It continued to float, and, at the end of the bloody three-day struggle that occurred after Emerson had gone, proclaimed the victory of the National Government.

Emerson went with Clough to many of the political clubs, intensely interested. The fire and fury of the people, he wrote home, would be inconceivable in New England. "All France is bearded like goats and lions... most of Paris is in some kind of uniform... everybody supposed to have a pistol in his pocket. But the deep sincerity of the speakers, who are agitating social, not political questions, and who are studying how to secure a fair share of bread to every man, and to get God's justice done through the land, is very good to hear."

Back to England for the lectures to be given in mid-June. But the course was less popular than perhaps any other Emerson had given or was to give; the theme was a cold one, and Emerson had treated it abstractly, without that kindling humanity which was usually so strong in his work, that deep underlying poetry that called out to his hearers like the sound of music. Nonetheless the speaker's extraordinary personal attraction, with his marvellous command of a flowing, harmonious English spoken in that unforgettable voice, were sufficient to win his audiences. The man was enough for them, even when what he said floated above their heads in the chill and lofty heights of the intellect.

On July 15, 1848, Emerson took passage home, this time in a paddlewheel steamer, one of the first to cross the seas. The voyage took only two weeks; two weeks that Emerson, still stoutly hating the sea, called "one long disgust." He was inexpressibly glad to be home; wanting, as he said, nothing better for the rest of his life than his own study, his books, the gentle Concord landscape, the friends and the neighbors, his wife and his children, with liberty to go on with his work.

Chapter XIV

Through the Fifties

EMERSON returned to an America harried over slavery, bitter with controversy. Shortly before he had reached home the Mexican War ended, bringing into the United States the immense territories now divided into the states of Arizona, New Mexico, Utah and California. Texas had already given up its brief independence under the Lone Star flag, and become a state in 1845. Under Mexican law slavery had been forbidden, but the South, desperately eager to regain its slipping power and dominance, was fighting for a congress and a president who would establish slavery as a law in the vast new territory, while the North was equally determined that what it felt to be an unholy institution should not be permitted to extend an inch further. The November elections of 1848 put Taylor, the Whig candidate, into the White House, a triumph for the Free Soil party. In that same year gold was discovered in California, the excitement rising fever-high in the following year. On September 8, 1850, California came to statehood with a constitution forbidding slavery under the approval of Taylor, enraging the South, which had borne the brunt of the fighting against Mexico and now saw the richest apple on the golden bough lost to it.

Ten days later, as a sop to Cerberus, Congress passed the Fugitive Slave Law, which took the work of catching escaping slaves and returning them to their masters out of the hands of the states, to put it under federal jurisdiction, thus nullifying both New York's and New England's refusal to act in fugitive slave cases, or to allow their jails to be used for the captured negroes. With the passage of the Act every citizen as well as every police officer in the land must help to surrender these fugitives to the law.

New England's great son, Daniel Webster, had championed this law with all his fiery eloquence in his famous Seventh of March speech, when he backed Clay's Compromise Bill, by virtue of which Congress was to keep its hands off the new territories as regarded the question of slavery, allowing each to become slaveholding or not as it chose. This speech and the resulting Fugitive Slave Act roused Emerson to a white heat of indignation. Up to 1850 Emerson had kept free from political interests; they had never, as he put it, "come near me, to my discomfort, before." Now, speaking to his neighbors at the Lyceum, he called it a "filthy law," telling his hearers "There is infamy in the air. I wake in the morning with a painful sensation which I carry about all day, and which, when traced home, is the ignominy which has fallen upon Massachusetts... The Act of Congress of September 18 is a law which every one of you will break on the earliest occasion—a law which no man can obey or abet the obeying without loss of self-respect and forfeiture of the name of a gentleman."

Webster was twenty-one years older than Emerson, and had been one of the heroes of Waldo's youth. But when, in 1843, Webster had come to Concord to argue a case at the courthouse, and to be welcomed by the Emersons as their house guest, the old spell was broken. Emerson still admired what he called his "splendid fire," and admitted that he appeared, among the best lawyers of the Suffolk bar, "like a schoolmaster amid his boys." But after attending the morning session he set down this criticism in his journal:

"One feels every moment that he goes for the actual world, and never for the ideal; perhaps it was this, perhaps it was a mark of having outlived some of my once finest pleasures, that I found no appetite to return to the court this afternoon. . . A very true and admirable man; I only wish he would not truckle."

There was no place in Emerson's world for the man who truckled. After Webster's sudden death in 1852, Emerson repeated his regret that he had sold himself to "the great and gross interests." The news had found him in Plymouth, where he was lecturing. Sitting on the shore, overlooking that historic bay, the philosopher set down this estimate of the dead man:

"Alas, he was the victim of his ambition; to please the South he betrayed the North, and was thrown out by both... (yet) *he was a statesman, and not the semblance of one. Most of our statesmen are in their places by luck or vulpine skill, not by any fitness. Webster was there for cause; the reality, the final person, who had to answer all the questions of the fainéants, and who had an answer."*

In 1849 Emerson brought out a new edition, with considerable added material, of his first book, *Nature.* In 1850 *Representative Men* was published. A book by him was now a major event, not only in America but in England, and these studies of epoch-making figures in the world's long story brought their author a popular as well as a distinguished praise.

One of the results was a widening of area in his annual lecture tours. In 1850 Emerson began the western journeys that were to last for twenty years, with some breaks during the War. His first trip took him as far as Michigan, which was as far as the railroad then reached. He returned to tell his Concord friends that America was interested in nothing but the railway. Walking with Ellery Channing through the beloved Concord fields he spoke of this obsession:

"On that one subject every man, woman and child is eloquent. Men stop you in the streets to tell you that the rails must come to their town or farmland. Laborers drop their tools to expatiate on the wonders and advantages of rail transportation, and women stand in the doorways of their bare and ugly homes with their eyes on the horizon, looking for the steam of the first locomotive. Like the Crusades in the Middle Ages, like art in Greece, railways occupy the soul and mind of America!"

It was late in the autumn but there yet lingered here and there among the sombre green of fir and pine a flash of gold or scarlet, and the cranberry bogs were yellow. A haze hung in the air, enhancing loveliness with mystery. As the two men sauntered down a country road Farmer Hosmer passed with his team, saluted them with a lifted hand, and drove on. Emerson turned to his friend:

"Ellery, we shall never see men like him, like Barrett, or Cyrus Hubbard, or Ephraim Wheeler, in the next generation. These old Saxons have the look of pine trees or apple trees, and might be the sons got between the two."

Ellery nodded:

"It's the railway, Waldo. It's too strong, corrupting the young farmers like a war, or the incursion of another race. The young men are mere amateurs, with an air their fathers never had." He added, with a touch of scorn: "They look as if they might be railway agents any day."

It was true. A great slow strength, a power of patience, a force capable of withstanding the assaults of hardship and meeting the demands of existence however stern with an indifferent humor, as part of the life of a man, were passing out of America. The century to come would see profound changes not only in the outward scene, the daily life of Americans, but in their character. Sensing this passing of an era, the friends stood silent, both feeling the poignancy of inevitable change. Certainly from where they stood in time the future looked to be filled with dangers. Ellery more than half believed it would succumb to them. Not so Emerson. His conviction that the balance was with good over evil, that the circle of human existence was not a mere circle but an uprising spiral, had not wavered. Man could meet his destiny and conquer it; conquer it though it killed him; rise above it and drag all life with him in the very moment of apparent loss, in the face of seeming defeat.

He stood on the mountains and looked afar off and was not frightened by what he saw. So it was that when he returned from the heights and spoke to men he brought them good tidings; was, as Hawthorne had said, one of the shining ones, or, in the words of Carlyle and Alexander Ireland, an angel.

Meanwhile the placid Concord life flowed sweetly on. Alcott, who had come another crash with his Fruitlands scheme, so serious a crash that the poor man almost lost his mind, had come back in 1844 from the town of Harvard, near which Fruitlands lay; that same little place where Emerson's father had begun, in want and anxiety, his career as a minister. Another windfall coming to Mrs. Alcott set the family again on its feet. They bought a small house not far from the Emersons, named it Hillside, and settled down for another spell of Concord. Alcott started a series of Thursday Talks, to which Concord came with a somewhat lessening enthusiasm and in decreasing numbers as time went on. For the philosopher's speech was so sublime as to be almost incomprehensible, and of a length past the ordinary person's endurance. "If," as Elizabeth Hoar said to Emerson, "he didn't talk so much, people would get so much more." Emerson was amused at these meetings by what he described as the festal and Olympian behavior of Mr. Alcott, and especially by his manner of greeting a newcomer, as though this fresh disciple appeared "large, sacred and crowned to him." On March 20, following Emerson's return from Europe, the last of these Thursdays took place, however, as the Alcotts were again on the wing, returning to Boston. They did not come back until 1857, although Alcott paid frequent visits to the village, and continued his occasional lectures for the Lyceum.

With the ever-increasing demands for lectures away from home Emerson was kept steadily at work while he remained there. He sat at his writing for six or even eight hours a day, beginning early in the morning, stopping for one o'clock dinner; and then, when he felt like it, putting in another hour or two in the afternoon. But he never worked in the evening, and was always in bed by half past ten. Answering the question of one of his visitors as to what he found best for an aid to his work, what most inspired him, he declared "There are two good things, sound sleep, and either a good book or a good companion, when it comes to writing, while for a successful lecture you need plenty of light, plenty of heat and plenty of people." He hated cold; hated the chill halls where he was sometimes called on to speak, or the ineffectual oil lamps that, in gasless towns, feebly glimmered over the audience and forced him to peer unhappily at his notes, almost indecipherable in the gloom.

The *Dial* had finally ceased to be. In the early part of its existence Carlyle had written to Emerson, commenting on the copies sent him, that the magazine was "all spirit-like, aëriform, aurora-borealis-like; no stalwart Yankee man with color in his cheeks and a coat on his back." Even after Margaret Fuller, exhausted by her work on it, had resigned it to Emerson, it remained vaporous, and with his departure for Europe began to fizzle toward its end.

Margaret had sailed for Europe the year before Emerson's departure. She had been on the editorial staff of the *Tribune*, under Horace Greeley, and had become a tempestuous figure in the literary world of America. An unhappy love affair complicated existence, family troubles wearied her. She felt she must have a change, freedom from weight of circumstances that were bearing her down. With letters from Emerson, from Greeley, from others, she sailed for England, went on to France, on to Italy. Here she fell in love with the Marquis d'Ossoli and was secretly married to him. The year later, 1848, she bore him a son, but the marriage remained unrevealed, and the child was put out to nurse in a hill town. Ossoli and Margaret became involved in the abortive attempt of Italy to free herself from the horrors of the Austrian oppression and were in the siege of Rome with Garibaldi and Mazzini. Margaret had met Mazzini in London, at the Carlyles', and revered him. When the city was taken these leaders had to flee, and after innumerable difficulties it became possible for the Ossolis to sail for America. They were almost penniless, and Margaret foresaw great anxieties once they were in her native land. The belated announcement of her marriage had upset her friends, shocked her family. The prospect of selling her book on the Italian Revolution was the only thing between starvation or dependence on her friends. Her child, roughly cared for by peasants, was sickly. Ossoli was devoted to her, but years younger, and there was no intellectual tie between the two. Could she hope to get back on the *Tribune*; to teach? And her husband, would there be any place for him in American life?

Come what might, America was better than Italy. The little family embarked for New York on May 17. At Gibraltar the captain died of smallpox and the little vessel was held in quarantine. It was July 15 before they reached America, driving before a hurricane. Next day the ship sank off Fire Island.

Margaret, who had met life boldly and freely, had gone suddenly and wildly to meet death, and with her her husband and her son.

"*Brave, eloquent, subtle soul,*" Emerson wrote. "*Margaret dies on the rocks of Fire Island beach, within sixty yards of the shore. As her life was romantic and exceptional, so let her death be. It sets the seal on her marriage; avoids all questions of society, all of employment, of poverty, of old age...*"

In 1852 the Hawthornes came back to Concord, bought the Alcott house and settled down, as they believed, permanently. Their oldest child, Una, was a year younger than Emerson's youngest, Edward, who was ten. Julian Hawthorne was seven, and there was a baby, Rose. Hawthorne by now had been received in both his own country and in England as an eminent writer. The success of his novel, *The Scarlet Letter*, had been immediate and astonishing. He was at last comfortably off and supremely happy in his family life. But his aversion from ordinary social intercourse remained much what it had been. He did not go to Concord's parties. He did, however, join his friends Thoreau, Ellery Channing or Emerson in their long, leisurely walks where the talk was apt to be less than the silences, and least of all from him. Emerson remarked to Ellery that a greater contrast than that between the present and the former owner of Hillside, which the Hawthornes had renamed Wayside, could be hardly imagined. Where Alcott, spouting words like an ever-flowing fountain, was full of futile plans for making Utopia spring from the dark, twisted root of the world, Hawthorne went withdrawn in a silent contemplation of the strange and troubled heart of man, confiding only to the written page his surmises and conclusions.

The Hawthornes' plans for remaining permanently in Concord were suddenly upset by Nathaniel's appointment as consul at Liverpool the year after their coming. In July 1853, they departed for an indefinite stay that extended to seven years. Hawthorne was indeed glad to get away from his native land. The increasing fury in political life that spread down through every rank and set friends and even families against each other, the endless stream of vituperation conducted by the press of the country, disgusted him. He saw in it the dusty battle of selfish interests ineffectually masking as redeemers and prophets, decrying each other and lying about themselves. England would be better than this.

Emerson felt much the same. He was constantly being urged to throw himself into the contest, and he confesses that he waked at night and bemoaned himself because he could not do so. But that churning pit of controversy was not for him. He admitted that the deplorable question of slavery needed a few assured voices, but his own work, he knew, by virtue of that inner guide in whose wisdom and good he so frankly believed, was not there. Though troubled at times:

"*In hours of sanity I recover myself, and say 'God must govern His own world, and know His way out of this pit, without my desertion of my post, which has none to guard it but me.' I have quite other slaves to free than these negroes, to wit, imprisoned spirits, imprisoned thoughts far back in the brain of man—far retired in the heaven of invention, and which, important in the Republic of Man, have no watchman, no lover or defender, but me.*"

Is there one among his countless readers who will not know him to have been right in this decision? Through these troubled years he was creating the essays that made up the volume of *English Traits*, published in 1856, and those that were collected under the title of *The Conduct of Life.* His lectures were being given in cities and in frontier posts, over the whole East and what was then known as the New West, and still beyond and further toward the sun. He spoke above the ephemeral passions of the day; put his emphasis on fundamentals; took his stand, as always, on the heights, with the simplicity, the nobility, that belonged there. Men, listening to the harmonies of that matchless voice, feeling the appeal to whatever was divine within them, went forth comforted, greater than they had come. No tilting in the noisy lists of politics could have done that.

During the summer of 1853 Emerson improved his house by building over the parlor, at the back, a large and pleasant room. Here Ellen, now at school in Lenox under a family friend, a Mrs. Sedgwick, would find herself installed on her return. In the attic, also, a small, secluded chamber was made for Emerson himself to retire to when he wished to be remote from household doings. By the end of September the noise and confusion was over, and the house at last exactly as he and Lydian wanted it. During a part of the time while the work was in progress Emerson was in Plymouth, Providence and Martha's Vineyard, lecturing. He was about to start west at the beginning of November when his mother, at the age of eighty-five, died as quietly, as gently, as she had lived. Her going was entirely unexpected, as Emerson wrote to Dr. Furness, his boyhood friend, in Philadelphia:

"*Mamma was made to live, and her death at eighty-five years took us by surprise. . . There was something majestic in those old frames built to live so tranquilly, usefully and kindly. The later generation seems to me to spend faster.*"

He wrote to Carlyle too, telling him that his mother's death had given him pain, in spite of her age, and quoting Elizabeth

Hoar, who had said "Mother's chamber was always radiant, because the pure in heart see God." Ever since Charles's death Ruth Haskins Emerson had been Mother to Elizabeth.

In 1855 Frank Sanborn came to Concord to live, having already visited there as a tutor to Emerson's children and those of his neighbors. Frank was an ardent friend to John Brown, then stirring up great trouble in Kansas, and brought that strange, ardent creature to speak in Concord, first in 1857, and again in 1859, shortly before the fight at Harper's Ferry and Brown's capture. Emerson had attended both talks, and had welcomed Brown as his guest. When Brown was lying under sentence of death in prison Emerson stepped into the arena of battle, as he had done after the passing of the Fugitive Slave Law, to tell Boston, under the subject "Courage," of "that new saint, than whom none purer and braver was ever led by love of men into conflict and death. The new saint, awaiting his martyrdom, and who, if he shall suffer, will make the gallows as glorious as the cross."

In 1857 the Alcotts came back, bought Orchard House, or Apple Slump as Louisa mischievously nicknamed it, close to The Wayside, and settled down for the rest of their lives. In June 1860, it was the Hawthornes' turn to come home. By now war was looming. No other end to the slavery question seemed longer possible. In January 1861, at Tremont Temple in Boston, an anti-slavery meeting was called where Emerson attempted to speak. But the hall was filled by a hoodlum crowd, against him, as it was against the Massachusetts Society that sponsored the meeting. He was howled down at each attempt he made, and finally left the building without having been permitted to say a word. He told Hawthorne later that although it was sorely against his personal inclination to appear at all, he was glad, glad to have at least "mowed and muttered," rather than not to have taken part in the demonstration.

In April Emerson began a new series of lectures in Boston, the first he had held there in two years. Sick of the compromises, the plots and counterplots, the endless moves met by countermoves, the underground railway with its necessity for hiding and skulking, he predicted in this lecture, with a profound sadness, "the downfall of our character-destroying civilization." People gasped at such a sentence from Emerson.

Two days later came the firing on Fort Sumter.

Emerson was content. Terrible as was war, there were worse things. He wrote a verse that spoke what he felt:

> *"Though love repine, and reason chafe,*
> *There came a voice without reply,—*
> *'Tis man's perdition to be safe,*
> *When for the truth he ought to die!"*

Chapter XV

War and Peace

The young men of Concord who were off for the war gathered in the Town Hall, with their relatives and friends, packing the main room, to hear the farewell addresses of Concord's great men, Judge Hoar, Alcott, Emerson. Prayers were said by the minister of the Unitarian Church, who recalled to his hearers how in 1775 their ancestors had been the first to take up arms in the sacred cause of freedom, and of how Emerson's grandfather, pastor of the same church of which himself was now minister, had been with difficulty restrained from snatching a gun and going forth with his flock to battle.

In his own brief address Emerson said that it was fit, if necessary, for a man to lay down his life for his beliefs, for the Cause that appeared to him the ultimate Good. War was an awful thing, but not the greatest calamity. "I have seen many a man and many a boy lounging in the streets outside the saloons, men and boys with no aim, no ideal, no call to any dedication beyond the moment's appetite, who needed but a master to make them useful to themselves and to society. War is such a master. It forces on the individual as on the State the larger view, the unselfish duty of coöperation, it appeals to the roots of strength within you, to the moral sense within you. Never, since I have read the papers, have I seen the morals play so large a part in them as now, nor seen in the face of every passerby the light of a resolution superior to all considerations of self."

Lincoln, though his election had been satisfactory to the North, was far as yet from being recognized as a great man. Emerson's own estimate at the time did not err on the side of enthusiasm. He wrote:

"*You cannot refine Mr. Lincoln's taste, extend his horizon, or clear his judgment; he will not walk dignifiedly through the traditional part of President of America, but will pop out his head at each railway station and make a little speech, and get into an argument with Squire A. and Judge B. He will write letters to Horace Greeley and any editor or reporter or saucy party committee that writes to him, and cheapen himself. But this we must be ready for, and let the clown appear, and hug ourselves that we are well off if we have got good nature, honest meaning, and fidelity to public interest, with bad manners—instead of an elegant roué and malignant self-seeker.*"

A good, honest, uncouth fellow! That was Boston's estimate, and Emerson was very much Boston. Had he not said, when asked, "I will tell you why I value Boston; because, when I go to enumerate its excellent names I do not take down the Boston Directory, but the National History to find them. . . Her ice burns more than other's fire."

Lincoln, a raw lawyer from the New West, had not yet taken his place in the National History, and could never take it in the Boston Directory.

The war, which everyone had supposed would be decided within a few months, dragged on its weary length of years. The stress of life intensified, money grew scarce; there were bank troubles, stocks and bonds fell, incomes were reduced. Emerson wrote Dr. Furness that his own resources had fallen almost to nothing. His son Edward could not have gone to college had it not been for the help of a wealthy friend. Lecture dates were naturally few, books sold but little. Living was put on the plainest basis. The young girls of the village, his Ellen, the Alcott sisters, Una Hawthorne among them, gathered at his house, or Orchard House or Wayside to roll bandages and engage in other war work. Packages were made up and sent each week to the front. Those boys still too young to be taken as soldiers were drilling under a sergeant who had been wounded and sent back. The older men took what share they could in furthering the cause of the North. Alcott went off to be chaplain; the farmers, with no young men to help, toiled to produce larger crops than before. The rest met the increased burden of taxation as best they might. Reverse after reverse fell on the North. Anxiety grew.

Emerson continued to write, and to speak whenever occasion offered. His faith never wavered, that small balance of good over evil, which he believed would triumph, as it had always in the long last triumphed. People went forth after hearing him refreshed, strengthened, as he had always strengthened and refreshed those to whom he spoke. His tall, slender figure, his austerely beautiful face, the spirit manifest in his blue eyes, the simple greatness of the man, carried authority. If this man did not speak truth, then there was no truth to speak!

It had become a habit for Emerson and a group of his friends to meet on Saturday nights in Boston for talk together over dinner. The Saturday Club they named it, and Emerson loved these "quiet, happy evenings with good speeches." Longfellow came to them from Cambridge, with James Russell Lowell, who had been editor of *The Atlantic Monthly* since its establishment in 1857 until the coming of war, and who was now expressing his pungent views in the pages of the *North American Review*, which publication he conducted with Charles Eliot Norton. During the war Lowell wrote almost entirely in prose, and was running his second series of *Biglow Papers* in the *Atlantic* at the same time with the criticisms in the *Review*. He had followed Longfellow as Professor of Modern Languages at Harvard, and was altogether a very busy man. Emerson delighted in his spontaneous wit.

Whittier, Edward Everett, Oliver Wendell Holmes, Cabot, who was to be Emerson's first biographer as he was his lifelong friend, Judge Hoar and other men of note made the meetings of the club the very heart of literary Boston. Emerson sat at what was called the Longfellow end of the table, speaking as was his wont in low tones to the men nearest him; picking and choosing his words, as Holmes, who was one of them, describes it, so that "to hear him talk was like watching someone crossing a brook on stepping stones." Emerson rarely made a speech at these meetings, preferring to be the listener. On one occasion when at his particular urging the club held a meeting in honor of Shakespeare's birthday, when suddenly called upon to respond to the toast to the Bard of Avon, he rose, beamed placidly around on the tableful of expectant faces, and then sat down again without having uttered a solitary word.

He had his own opinion about the inveterate American custom of after-dinner speaking. "It is an American vice," he remarked, on one of the few occasions when the Hawthornes had come for an evening at his house. "Most of us are overexpressed, beaten out thin, all surface without depth or substance. We do not absorb and make flesh of the thoughts that wander through our minds but report them as thoughts, retail them as stimulating news. At a dreadful cost of national shallowness we play this game."

Hawthorne could agree with that. He had never willingly made a speech in his life, and the half dozen to his credit were spoken in his person as Consul, and not to be avoided.

At the Saturday Club, however, the speeches were not shallow utterances but sound and considered thought, ripely and usually wittily expressed. Emerson used to sit listening, his shoulders hunched, his head slightly advanced, looking like an eagle perched on its eyrie; his eyes, so Holmes said, "watching the flight of a thought as though it were his prey, to be seized in mid-air and carried off."

With the year 1862 the North began to turn the tide in her favor, and on January 1st, 1863 came Lincoln's Proclamation of Emancipation, to the great satisfaction of all New England. While this proclamation was still in abeyance there were many in the North who opposed it, among them George Francis Train, who at a great public meeting in New York shouted that slavery was a divine institution. "So," cried an old man, rising in the audience, "is Hell." The papers took this up and Emerson chuckled over it with amused appreciation, jotting it down in his journal. A forthright expression of opinion always delighted him.

The first break in the small Concord group had come in May 1862, with the death of Henry David Thoreau at the age of forty-five. He had been ill for more than a year, having caught a chill while studying the rings in one of the ancient trees that had been felled in the winter woods. The tuberculosis latent in him had developed, and after a fruitless stay in Minnesota he had come home to die. Ellery Channing, who preferred him above any other of his friends, but who was no longer living in Concord, made it a point to come to see him as often as possible. On a September day the two walked together for the last time to Walden Pond, where the stoutly built shack in which Henry had passed his two hermit years still stood. Thoreau, gaunt and pallid, smiled at the little shelter in that lovely and quiet place, and spoke to his friend of the happiness of those vanished months. "Someone said once that I believed Nature was invented in Concord, Ellery, and I think I do."

One of Henry's staunchest friends was Sam Staples, the sheriff.

Sam had had to arrest Henry once, when, as a stand against tyranny, he had refused, together with Alcott, to pay his taxes. That was Sam's duty, and Henry accepted it as such. It made no difference in their friendship, and later, when Thoreau became a surveyor, Sam was usually along to help with rod and chain. After the dying man could no longer go abroad Sam was one of his most faithful visitors and one day, meeting Emerson in the village after such a call, he remarked:

"I've just come from a visit with our friend, Mr. Emerson, and I want to tell you that I never spent a more satisfactory hour, nor ever saw a man dying with so much pleasure and peace as Mr. Thoreau."

He was the first of the Transcendentalists to be buried in the newly consecrated cemetery of Sleepy Hollow. A year later, in the same month of May, Emerson's Aunt Mary followed him, to lie in the Emerson lot. The last three or four years of her long life – she was eighty-nine – had been spent in the home of a niece in Williamsburg, now part of Brooklyn, New York. This strange, difficult, but fascinating woman had lived her life in a constant war against, as one who loved her well, Sarah Ripley, said, "all the decorums of society. She eats and drinks what others do not, and when they do not; dresses in white these October days, enters into conversation with everybody, and talks on every subject; is sharp as a razor in her satire, and sees you through and through in a moment."

She had been furious with Emerson when he left the ministry, scornful of what she called his vagaries of thought and idea. For a long while she refused not only to visit him, but even to come to Concord, since he lived there. Finally she appeared unannounced and walked into his study as though nothing had happened. He greeted her serenely, and presently took her into the parlor, where Lydian was entertaining two or three friends. Aunt Mary, the introductions over, seated herself and looked sternly upon Lydian. Aunt Mary believed that an Emerson stood at the head of all New England's aristocracy of brain and breeding and intended to be sure that this niece by marriage realized what that meant.

"Lydia Jackson," she said, in the clear, sharp voice Emerson knew only too well, "I trust you realize that though you are *among* us, you are not *of* us."

Lydian, who had plenty of the saving grace of humor, agreed that was a condition she could not hope to change, and delighted in Aunt Mary from that moment on.

The New England propensity to save had reached its height in Aunt Mary. Emerson, in the account he wrote of her after her death, tells us that she wasted nothing, not even medicine. Medicine was to be taken. Consequently, "If she found a pill here, another there, a drop of laudanum, a little quinine, she mixed them all together, and swallowed them."

Truly a daughter of New England in all that meant of originality, force, intellect, absurdity. Impossible to get along with; capable of any sacrifice but her own way; mean in small things and generous in great ones; proud of her family; critical of its members; always called on to come when there was illness or when help was wanted, nursing an insane relative for years; she had kept her spirit to the last, and gone down to death with colors flying.

There seemed something fatal in the month of May, for in the year following it was Hawthorne they brought to be buried in Sleepy Hollow. Here is how Emerson wrote of the event:

"In a pomp of sunshine and verdure and gentle winds Hawthorne is buried. James Freeman Clarke read the services, in the church and at the grave. Longfellow, Holmes, Lowell, Agassiz, Hoar, Dwight, Whipple, Norton, Alcott, Hillard, Fields, Judge Thomas and Emerson pallbearers. Franklin Pierce with the family. The church decorated with white flowers, delicately arranged. The body unwillingly shown – only a few minutes to this company of his friends. Hawthorne was noble and serene in aspect . . . a calm and powerful head. . . A large company filled church and cemetery. All was so bright and hopeful that pain or mourning were hardly suggested, and Holmes said 'It looks like a happy meeting.'"

Emerson regretted that he had never come to know Hawthorne better, feeling that both men had somehow missed each other, and that this was a pity.

This was during the last year of the war, 1864. In the winter just past, Ralph Waldo's brother William had lost his eldest son, another sacrifice to tuberculosis. The young man had been married but a few months and stood on the threshold of what appeared to be a brilliant career in the law. William was greatly broken by the loss. He came to spend part of the summer at his brother's in Concord, and Emerson, meeting him at the station, saw an old man get off the train. The six months since his son's death had added ten years to William's age. Both of his remaining sons were at the front, one a surgeon under Grant. They came through safely.

In September Agassiz, who was working heart and soul to establish an agricultural college at Harvard, also came to stay with the Emersons. He was a most engaging man, a wonderful talker, at ease in any society, a man full of enthusiasm, of laughter. Ellery Channing returned to Concord this year and the three men resumed the long walks Emerson loved. It was a very dry fall, marching toward winter in a perfect blaze of color. For the first time in memory the river meadows had dried out; you could tramp over them in any direction; the river had shrunk under its lily pads and moved so slowly that the gold and scarlet of fallen leaves scarcely drifted past the banks. The passenger birds were flying, and Agassiz could name them one and all. Each day there was a new panorama. Beauty walked the hills, the woods, the fields, and painted the skies. Amid all the changing hues the gray rocks and the dark hemlocks struck their own steadfast note.

"Thoreau should be with us," Ellery said, on one of these enchanted days. "How he loved the reflections of those dark trees in the river. He told me the Indians called it the *Muskéeticock*, meaning Dead Water. And I remember he told me that the Indians brew a tea from the hemlock needles that is not at all bad. He said it was a delightful thing to see a great handful of the branch tips boiling in the pot over the camp fire."

"Thoreau's patience with nature was one of his most astonishing characteristics," Emerson said. "The man who was never so good in conversation as when roused to argument, who was quick and impatient with his fellow men, this man could sit motionless for hours studying an insect, a bird, an animal, a plant, contented and at peace."

"He trusted nature and mistrusted man," was Agassiz' comment. "He knew the first far better than the second, and in spite of the cynics, it is what we know best that we trust."

They walked on, musing of the friends who had, with them, known the familiar loveliness of these scenes; Thoreau, Hawthorne, Emerson's brother Charles, these had gone on, never to return. They, like the three friends now strolling together through the glory of the dying year, had pondered deeply on the mystery that is man's life and had brought their different answers before leaving life behind. Yet the mystery remained.

"My answer, too, will not solve it," Emerson thought. "For me, possibly, but not for others. All I can do, all any man can do, is to indicate a path, a direction which other men may follow to their own discoveries, their own conclusions. I pretend to no more, and I have never wanted a disciple, never uttered a dogma. Freedom is what I want, for others as for myself. Did not Christ himself say, 'In my Father's house are many mansions'?"

Before the beginning of war Emerson had met, while filling a lecture engagement at Naushon, a man whom he described as "the only Esquire of Massachusetts." This man was John Murray Forbes, an administrator of railways, a man of wealth, distinction and unusual charm. Emerson loved him at once, and his family with him. His son, William Hathaway, became a major during the war, and was taken prisoner in a hand-to-hand conflict at Columbia, S. C., by Mosby's Guerillas, having been pinned underneath his fallen horse. After escaping only to be recaptured, the young cavalry officer was paroled in March 1865, and after a stay with his own family, came to visit the Emersons. It was not the first time he had been there, and very soon he and Emerson's younger daughter, Edith, announced their engagement. She was twenty-three, Forbes some few years older. Both families were delighted.

The engagement had hardly been announced before news came that the young man had been exchanged, and released from parole. He was advanced to the rank of lieutenant colonel and went at once to join his command. He arrived just in time for Lee's surrender. The war was over.

That October, at a simple ceremony in the Emerson house, the two young people were wedded. The marriage was in every way happy and successful. Moreover, it brought into the Emerson family what it had never known before, an excellent man of business.

Thanksgiving, that November, was celebrated all over the North with a deep sense of blessing. To the Emerson feast came the whole of the Forbes and Jackson families, making a great circle. Sarah Ripley was there too, she and Lydian's brother, Dr. Jackson, keeping the table laughing with their ready wit. Sarah was still living at the Old Manse, which was always full of members of her family and was a great gathering place for the young folk of the village, for she delighted in giving parties.

"Sarah, you know more and let it weigh on you less than any other woman in the world," the Doctor told her.

"I've only studied what I loved, and love burdens no one," she answered.

"Yes, it is those who love what they do who do the things worth doing," Emerson agreed, "and who are not burdened by what they do." He told of having met in England George Stephenson, the engineer and inventor who had built the *Rocket*, the first practical locomotive, and made railway travel possible.

"He was one of the most interesting and remarkable men in England, and to talk with him was to experience an education in wisdom and sense. Yet at the age of seventeen he could not read. It was his love for the inventions of Watt that started him on his career. He studied what he loved, and all else needed to make that study effective. There was the properly educated man. Stuffing dry facts into indifferent students is not education, yet that is what our institutions of learning confine themselves to doing."

"You're right," Forbes assented. "But the locomotive isn't the only invention that has changed the habits of civilized man since our youth, Waldo."

"I say there have been five miracles in my time," Emerson answered. "The steamboat, the railway, the telegraph, the photograph, and the application of the spectroscope to astronomy, with all its revelations concerning the construction of the universe."

"And there's the power press, and the power loom, and your

own discovery of anæsthesia, Doctor," said young Edward Emerson, up from Harvard.

"And the machine for pegging shoes," laughed Lydian, "and the steel pen, though Waldo sticks to the quill."

"There isn't a worse nuisance to a writer than a steel pen. I've tried one and know," Emerson declared.

"There are other inventions we can't get into use, proved though they've been," Dr. Jackson informed them. "There's the turbine engine, which saves ninety-seven per cent of the power of a waterfall, for one ; and the chimney that can burn its own smoke and keep the air free of soot, for another. In a hundred years, perhaps, the general intelligence will have reached the point when it will insist on having these put into service. The other inventions have had to wait about that length of time."

"Perhaps that is well," Emerson answered slowly. "Every new invention is potent for danger as well as for good. A man must not be rushed too fast. The coming of peace has brought new, great problems. These machines, and those to be developed, will give our sons another world from the one we've known, to live in and to conquer. Don't be impatient, you scientists, to hurry the tide."

Chapter XVI

From Coast to Coast they knew his Name

There was a magical quality to Ralph Waldo Emerson. A highly cultivated, quiet, reserved man, bred as a minister in the most conservative corner of the United States, his interests were devoted to the moral principles that govern the life of man. He spoke and wrote of the "oversoul," of the divinity within each individual, of the exquisite relationships of the spirit with nature. He was concerned with the conduct of life, with man's goodness, his fineness. Nowhere did he advise anyone how to better his material condition, nor did he ever tell a story. He disclaimed all leadership, wishing men not to come to him but to go to themselves for guidance. There was nothing spectacular about him, no dizzy flights of oratory in his delivery.

And yet the name of this man was known from coast to coast. It was known throughout the British Isles, in Canada; it was beginning to be known on the Continent of Europe. From 1850 to 1870, even to a considerable extent through the years of the war, he was welcomed not only in such cities as Boston, New York, Washington, Baltimore, Montreal, Philadelphia, but in the raw wooden shanty towns of the new West; in frontier communities beyond the railroad, where, as he said himself, the only apparent interest was in prices, and in sections and quarter sections of untilled land; and where the "kind and well disposed people in all that is called cultivation are only ten years old."

Why did these people crowd as eagerly into the ill-lighted and ill-heated shacks of their prairie towns to listen to Emerson as did the trained audiences of the Eastern cities into their fine auditoriums? Probably not half a dozen among those farmer listeners in each place where he lectured had read even one of his few books. But year after year, on tours that sometimes lasted for nearly three winter months, Emerson traveled far and near over the country with a notable success. There was no blare of publicity, no shrieking signs, no sensational appeal. Committees wrote to him, dates were settled, the local paper announced his coming.

"They say to me, these committees," Emerson, amused, told Lydian, "that what their 'folks' want is a hearty laugh. But I have no material for hearty laughs. I can put in a few allusions, tell a few anecdotes that might bring a chuckle, and I do that much for them. Roars of laughter will never, however, convulse any audience of mine."

"Yet they keep on wanting you."

They did. And it was these tours that provided the major part of Emerson's income. But it was a wearisome business. He didn't want to lecture, he wanted to write. He didn't want to travel, he preferred to remain at home. But he must earn money, and as he put it, with his unfailing glint of humor, "this dragging of a decorous old gentleman out of home and out of position to a juvenile career" amounted to a wager between himself and the organizer of a tour. This organizer says, " 'I'll bet you fifty dollars a day for three weeks that you will not leave your library and wade, and freeze, and ride, and run, and suffer all manner of indignities, and stand up for an hour each night reading in a hall.' And I answer, 'I'll bet I will.' I do it, and win the nine hundred dollars."

This explanation is all very well for a joke. But what was the urge that led America, even the raw America of the West, to demand this "decorous old gentleman," as he calls himself, again and again? Surely much that he spoke must have been beyond the understanding of most of his hearers. We can read those lectures today, refined and polished in the writing, with the humorous "allusions and anecdotes" deleted, to be sure, in the volumes of his essays, and find them full of the wisdom that is Emerson, wisdom that shines against a background of the widest reading, that is the product of the deepest thought of the philosopher he was. Was it this wisdom that won his audiences wherever he went, was it this grace of language, this ordered thought?

There was more than these. There was that something in the man that made him appear the bringer of good tidings, and not merely generally, but specially and to you. Those who heard him might not always grasp the exact meaning of his message, but each felt, listening, that there was a glory in being a man or a woman; that the shallow troubles and small bitternesses of life lost their seeming importance; that during the hour while Emerson spoke they had moved, individually, into a fresher, larger place, into nobility. This was his magic: that he lifted up the hearts of his hearers and led them out of the earth into the heaven of their own being.

Much of this power is in his words. We read him today, fifty years and more since his death, and find it; but there was yet more in the man himself. There was in him the positive power of a great goodness, a great kindness that no one could miss. There was his faith that man was the child of God, harboring divinity within himself; his conviction that plain living was no bar to high thinking, that even "in the mud and scum of things," lay some hint of beauty, some possibility of happiness; these, and his singular charm, his unforgettable voice, his countenance, with its compound of austerity and friendliness, of shyness and serenity. Having heard him, you wished to hear him again; having only heard about him, what you heard made you long to listen to the man himself.

We get glimpses of him on his tours, traveling under the hardships of those days. Crouched unhappily on a hard seat through long nights of railway journeying, for there were no sleepers. On a boat between Philadelphia and Pittsburgh where "we slept on the floor, each of us receiving a long narrow cushion to lie on. There was no room to spare, I slept in a wreath of legs, the knees of another sleeper crossing mine." In a temperature near zero he is ferried across the Missouri in a small open boat, dodging cakes of ice, almost climbing over ice floes. In sleighs he is drawn over the prairies while a bitter wind blows in his face and the flying snow blinds him. In small towns he makes his way to the hall along narrow wooden pavements where, should he step off, he would "sink to the shoulders in mud." Through Ohio, through Illinois to thriving, quick-growing Chicago; stopping at many a small town en route; on as far as St. Paul and Minneapolis, which latter city he found to be handsome and attractive; through Kansas, to Milwaukee; back and forth he went over this "America in the raw, America in the making," as he described it. Until 1866 he managed his tours as well as he might himself, but then his son-in-law took the business management of the Emerson family into his clever and capable hands. He found an excellent agent who took over all the labor of arranging schedules, train trips, stops, funds; and who even had hotels and carriages waiting for the guest instead of leaving to chance and the last minute these necessities to comfort. Colonel Forbes did more than this. He overhauled the book contracts and greatly improved the income from that source; and he saved, in the very nick of time, the small property belonging to Lydian from the hands of a dishonest agent. By the end of 1867 Emerson found his finances so much improved, in fact, that he refused to make any more far western tours. In 1870 he went to California. But this was not as a lecturer, though he spoke in San Francisco. He traveled as the guest of Mr. John Forbes, that "Esquire" of Massachusetts, Edith's father-in-law and his good friend, and in that gentleman's private car.

This trip had been engineered between Lydian and Forbes largely for Emerson's sake. He had not been very well through the winter and with April his lassitude and reluctance to leave the house, even when the spring grew lovely, alarmed the family. Forbes made all the arrangements and then came down to Concord to persuade Emerson to become his guest. There were to be several good friends of the Concord Sage in the party, among them his daughter and her husband; Garth Wilkinson James, James B. Thayer, Royall Professor of Law at Cambridge, and a Mrs. George Russell, a lively, interesting and sensible woman. Lydian, who had not been in robust health since the birth of Edward, could not be persuaded to leave her beloved home, and it took a great deal of effort to win Emerson's consent. He did not like to be beholden even to his friends, and it was only Edith's firm declaration that unless he went she too would refuse that broke down his resistance. Once the matter was settled he was as happy as a child, and before the journey was two days old he was in the best of spirits. No one had ever heard him talk so much or so gaily, and nothing tired him. He enjoyed the luxury of the car, the company of his friends, the scenery, the release from all responsibility, whole-heartedly. At Salt Lake City he was greatly interested in meeting Brigham Young and seeing the wonders of the desert oasis the prophet had set up. California was reached in all the splendor of her springtide, and Emerson went quite wild over the wonder of the flower-sheeted mountains. He liked the good sound wine too; remarked on the cheapness of grapes in that blessed climate, where "there being really nothing cheaper than grape juice with grapes a cent a pound there is no reason for adulterating the wine."

It took the party eleven days to make the trip across the continent and reach San Francisco, where they put up at the Occidental Hotel. This was Friday, and on Sunday Emerson was asked to lecture in the evening at the Unitarian Church by the minister, Reverend Horatio Stebbins, successor to Starr King. Emerson chose to give his talk on "Immortality" and spoke to a packed audience. The next day the *Alta California* published a report of the address full of high-sounding praise, and Emerson chuckled aloud as he read it, especially when he reached the final paragraph, which ran in this wise:

"*All left the church feeling that an elegant tribute had been paid to the creative genius of the Great First Cause, and that a masterly use of the English language had been made to that end.*"

Ten days were devoted to seeing San Francisco and the Peninsula, the valleys to the south, the Contra Costa hills, and to meeting people to whom the name of Emerson was already a beloved one. There were many New Englanders among them, forty-niners or their sons, sea captains who had left the sea, traders who had followed the adventurers, and were now the owners of profitable businesses. Here and there was a name later to be known in the world of art and literature. It was a different population from that of the middle west, a cosmopolitan society here on the ultimate western edge of the continent.

The party left for Yosemite Valley on May 2 with horses, taking three and a half days for the trip, and going to the hotel known as Leidig's Tavern. At that time John Muir was in the valley, partly because it was, as he said, the grand vestibule of the Sierra, partly because he needed money, and was running a sawmill he had built to saw fallen timber for building cottages.

Going to the hotel for provisions, the young Scot, (he was

thirty-three at that date) heard the people saying, "with solemn emphasis, 'Emerson is here!'" And he tells us then how he felt:

"I was excited as I had never been excited before, and my heart throbbed as if an angel direct from Heaven had alighted on the Sierran rocks. But so great was my awe and reverence, I did not dare to go to him or speak to him. I hovered on the outside of the crowd of people that were pressing forward to be introduced to him, and shaking hands with him. Then I heard that in three or four days he was going away, and in the course of sheer desperation I wrote him a note and carried it to his hotel telling him that El Capitan and Tissiac demanded him to stay longer."

Emerson liked that letter so well that the next morning he asked where he could find the writer, and was directed to the sawmill. Mounting the piebald pony that had been assigned for his use, he took Professor Thayer with him and rode across the valley. Thayer hailed the mill when they reached it, for no one was in sight. Muir stepped out: and now let him take up the story again:

"Emerson said, 'Why did you not make yourself known last evening? I should have been very glad to have seen you.' Then he dismounted and came into the mill. I had a study attached to the gable of the mill, overhanging the stream, into which I invited him, but it was not easy of access, being reached only by a series of sloping planks roughened by slats like a hen ladder; but he bravely climbed up and I showed him my collection of plants and sketches drawn from the surrounding mountains, and he asked many questions, pumping unconsciously.

"He came again and again, and I saw him every day he remained in the valley, and on leaving I was invited to accompany him as far as the Mariposa Grove of Big Trees. I said, 'I'll go, Mr. Emerson, if you will promise to camp with me in the grove. I'll build a glorious camp fire, and the great brown boles of the giant Sequoias will be most impressively lighted up, and the night will be glorious.' At this he became enthusiastic like a boy, his sweet, perennial smile became deeper and sweeter, and he said, 'Yes, yes, we will camp out, camp out.' So next day we left Yosemite and rode twenty-five miles through the Sierra forests, the noblest on the face of the earth, and he kept me talking all the time, but said little himself."

Alas for Muir's fine plan. When the party reached Clark's Station, now Wawona Lodge, they began dismounting. Surprised, he asked whether they were not going on to camp under the sequoias. They drew him aside, hushed him:

"No, it would never do to lie out in the night air. Mr. Emerson might take cold, and you know, Mr. Muir, that would be a dreadful thing."

In vain Muir urged that only in hotels and homes were colds caught, and that nobody was ever known to take cold camping in those woods. "There was not a single sneeze or cough in the whole of the Sierra," he insisted, pathetically eager to get his hero out for one great night with nature, to make, as he said, "an immortal Emerson night of it." He goes on: "*But the house habit was not to be overcome, and the carpet dust and unknowable reeks were preferred to the beauty and fragrance of Sequoia flame.*"

Emerson was, as Muir realized, in the hands of his friends, "his affectionate but sadly civilized friends." The following day they rode on to Mariposa, where Mr. Galen Clark, guardian of the grove, "selected the finest of the unnamed trees, and requested Emerson to give it a name. He named it Samoset, after the New England sachem."

Then the party rode out, Muir going as far as the edge of the grove with them. On they went, up the slope to the top of the ridge. Emerson had lingered behind, and after all but he had disappeared he stopped, turned his horse, and taking off his hat, waved a salute, a last good-bye.

Muir went back to make his fire, and his camp, which was only a fold in the bark of a sequoia. He was lonely, "*lonesome for the first time in these forests,* (*but*) *I quickly took heart again—the trees had not gone to Boston, nor the birds; and as I sat by the fire, Emerson was still with me in spirit, though I never saw him again in the flesh.*"

Though they never met again, they exchanged a few letters, and Muir sent his friend a cluster of the golden sprays of the blossoms of the incense cedar, that blooms in January amid the snow, having climbed one of the splendid trees to gather them. In sending his thanks Emerson wrote:

"*I have everywhere testified to my friends, who should also be yours, my happiness in finding you, the right man in the right place.*"

He stopped, turned his horse, and taking off his hat, waved a salute, a last good-bye

CHAPTER XVII

Over the Winter Glaciers
I see the Summer glow. . .

ON the anniversary of his sixtieth year Emerson wrote the lines from which the two at the head of this chapter are quoted. They express the same feeling as that which he set down in prose: "Within I do not find wrinkles and a used heart, but unspent youth." He was to the end unconquerably young, in spite of the failing memory that began to trouble him in 1872, and increased thereafter with each year.

In 1860 he had published the volume of essays called *The Conduct of Life*. Ten years later came *Society and Solitude*, and in 1876 the miscellaneous collection appearing under the title *Letters and Social Aims*. In 1866 he brought out his second and last book of verse, *May Day*. In this the poem "Terminus" was published for the first time. These steady, serenely hopeful lines describe the last lap of his life voyage with a clear beauty:

"*It is time to be old,*
To take in sail:—
The god of bounds,
Who sets to seas a shore,
Came to me in his fatal rounds,
And said: 'No more!'

* * *

As the bird trims her to the gale,
I trim myself to the storms of time,

I man the rudder, reef the sail,
Obey the voice at eve obeyed at prime:
'Lowly faithful, banish fear,
Right onward drive unharmed;
The port, well worth the cruise, is near,
And every wave is charmed.'"

In these lines, as in the anniversary poem, there is nothing aged, nothing worn. Sunset is nearing, it is time to reach home, but courage, hope and faith are strong as ever.

The last part of his life was given a fresh happiness by his grandchildren. The first, a boy, was born in 1866, the same year in which his last remaining brother, William, died. Compensation, joy balancing grief, a new gift for a loss. He was never happier, as time went on, than in watching Edith's children at play.

"I like to see how children are encouraged nowadays," he told his daughter. "Taught how to play and be happy. I found my own childhood first with my little Wallie, and then with the rest of you. And now these happy children of yours surround me."

"They cannot be more happy than we were, Father. No children were ever happier."

He nodded.

"Yes, I remember once, on a visit to William, when you and your cousins were all young, telling him that our babes were having a happy childhood, with no cruel interference, but a store of happy days. It pleased him, for it was true of both our families."

Emerson had been made one of the Overseers of Harvard in 1867, receiving at the same time the honorary degree of LL.D. For twelve years he served his Alma Mater, rarely missing a meeting, working always for the broadening of the curriculum and a greater individual freedom. It was he who insisted on having the outworn system of marking for deportment abolished. In addition he gave two series of lectures, in 1869 and 1870, to a class of some thirty students. He took for his theme the subject he had used in England, the "Natural History of the Intellect." He was disappointed in his work, however, though the young men who came to hear him found the talks inspiring. Indeed, he thanked them for the regularity of their attendance and the interest they had shown. But, after delivering the final one, he came home, looking depressed.

"Queenie, (his nickname for Lydian) Queenie, my dear, I've joined the 'dim choir of the bards who have been,' and there's no trying to disguise the fact."

She smiled. "When were you ever satisfied with your work? The boys loved you."

But it was this failure, for such it seemed to him, which had so worn on him that the trip to California had been decided upon.

In the October following his return from that trip the terrible fire that laid Chicago in ashes shocked the nation. In November the stricken city was already at work rebuilding. It sent an appeal to Emerson to come and speak in the big impromptu auditorium set up for public meetings. Although he had definitely given up his western trips, he could not refuse this call. When he rose to speak he was greeted by long, thundering applause, and stood, pale and greatly moved by the tremendous ovation, his head slightly bowed and turned to one side.

Whatever he said, whatever was reported about him, was now eagerly listened to, widely read. In January 1872 he gave two lectures, one in Baltimore, the other in Washington for the Howard University for Freedmen, an institution for negroes. In this talk he quoted from a poem by George Herbert, and when he found there was no copy of Herbert's verse in the university library he promised to send a copy. When he returned to Boston he went to the nearest bookstore to redeem his promise. But the lecture had been fully reported in the papers, and there was no copy of Herbert to be found in that or a half dozen other bookshops.

"We are all sold out, sir, the rush for them has been so great," he was told.

His older daughter, Ellen, had been with him on these trips and when, in the late spring of this year he agreed to give a series of six readings from English Prose and Verse at the Mechanics' Hall, Boston, got up by his old friend, the publisher, James T. Fields, she was always beside him. He had already been troubled with an inability to remember the word he wanted, and this grew more noticeable in the Boston lectures. Once he reread an entire page without realizing it. This troubled Ellen, but when she spoke to her father, trying to plan some method by which such slips could be avoided, he only smiled:

"My dear, things that go wrong about these lectures don't disturb me, because I know that everyone knows that I am worn out and passed by, and that it is only my old friends, come for friendship's sake to have one last season with me, who are here in the hall."

It *was* friends, old and new. Every seat for all six readings was sold out before the first reading was given, and Boston's ice, which Emerson had said burned more than other's fire, was surely warm and glowing throughout this last of his many series of lectures.

In 1868 Louisa Alcott had made her great success with *Little Women*, repeating this in 1871 with *Little Men*. All Concord rejoiced with her, and no one more than her friend, Ralph Waldo Emerson. Through all her life he was to her the best friend she had known, and it was only by a few years that she survived him. Thanks to her success the Alcott difficulties were at an end. Her two surviving sisters had married, and she took care of her father after her mother's death to the day he died, dying unexpectedly herself two days after.

The Orchard House was overflowing with nephews and nieces by the time *Little Men* came out, and the Emersons gave a big party in honor of it to which these youngsters and all the neighborhood children were invited. These children's festivals were one of the delights of the Emerson home, and were kept up to the very last year of his life. There would be games, and a lovely tea, and Ellen would supervise, and Emerson come in, tall, stooping, kindly with a heaven-graciousness; and often there were funny little gifts to take away, which he would hand out. That he could not remember names or sometimes forgot he had given one child its gift already, and gave it another, made no difference in the general joy. No child who was at one of the Emerson parties ever forgot it in later years.

Life was flowing on serenely. Edward, the son of the house, had been through a slight operation successfully, and in May sailed for a rest in Europe with his sister Edith and the Colonel. Lydian, though always something of an invalid, was yet bearing herself comfortably. During their parents' trip abroad Edith's children were with their grandparents, Mr. and Mrs. Forbes, at the charming house built by the Colonel at Naushon-on-the-Sea, and there Ellen went for a visit. She had found a cook and general housemaid in Boston to do the needed work in the Concord house while the two regular servants were given a holiday. A middle-aged, well-recommended woman.

On July 24, at about half past five in the morning, Emerson was wakened by a sharp crackling sound. As he sat up in bed the smell of burning wood reached him and then, through a slit in the door of a closet beside the chimney piece, he saw the glint of fire. Quickly rousing his wife, the two got themselves hurriedly into a few clothes and ran downstairs. A misty rain was falling through which Emerson dashed to the front gate and cried "*Fire, Fire*" at the full pitch of that great voice. It carried far, reaching several neighbors, who instantly responded, men in hastily pulled-on shirts and trousers, some still barefooted, arriving at top speed, women ringing bells on their porches, calling out, sending children flying to summon every possible help. Before the fire company reached the scene, which it did with astonishing promptness, rescue work was already organized. Men and boys with wet cloths bound over their heads were dashing in and out carrying furniture, pictures, ornaments, placing these at a safe distance, while the women gathered up what was likely to be hurt by the wet and carted it off to the nearest shelter. The garret had been the starting place of the fire, and here the first work was done, boxes of valuable papers being thrown out of the windows helter-skelter before the flames and smoke drove the rescuers down. The firemen got the hose going but it was not till half past eight that the fire was at last completely quenched. By then the roof had fallen in and the house was gutted.

The good sense, courage and clear-headedness of the Concord folk were nevertheless rewarded. Almost everything inside had been saved that was not nailed down. Even the papers which were so close to Emerson's heart, even the books that were part of his life. The rain had ceased early, and before the firemen's hose did harm to the lower floor everything perishable was safe.

But the house, the beloved house, stood ghastly and forlorn, only the walls and the lower rooms intact, and they ruined by water and smoke. Fortunately the trees Emerson had planted and tended to their fine maturity were saved from serious damage by the wet weather. It was found later that the serving-woman, prowling in the garret with a candle, had started the blaze.

Once the fire was out Judge Keyes, whose carriage was waiting, got the two Emersons into it and took them to his house, where dry clothes, (for both were drenched to the skin), and a hot breakfast waited. After that was eaten they were persuaded to go to bed, worn out by the emotional shock and their exertions; Emerson in particular having toiled to gather up the scattered papers before the wind should carry them away. Offers came from almost everyone in the town to make their home where they wished, but it was to the Old Manse that they went next day, sufficiently recovered to make the change, though Emerson had developed a feverish cold. Sarah was away and the Manse was then the home of a cousin, Elizabeth Ripley, and full of her family. There was a bedroom available, but no study in which Emerson could work. He had been deep in the preparation of a book promised an English publisher by a certain date, and in spite of the calamity he wanted to keep the engagement. The need for working space was instantly met. A room in the Court House was assigned to him, all his study furnishings and what books he needed moved in. He began work at once.

Meanwhile Emerson's nearest friends got together to see what could be done to meet the situation. One of them, who had been a classmate at Harvard, James Cabot Lowell of Waltham, came the day after the fire to offer his friends his own home. But they preferred to remain at the Manse. He found Emerson looking badly, evidently exhausted.

"You ought to be in bed, man."

"It is easier to stay out of bed than to get out if you once yield. I've always hated a day in bed, James, and I see no reason, because my house has burned down, to climb into one now. No. Besides, there's the book."

"He cannot be persuaded," Lydian told the visitor, when he spoke with her alone. "And I think this work is a real help to him. He will bury himself in it, and the shock will be eased. Then we shall have to think of what we must do, and that will inspire him. I have never seen him take to his bed, not even at a time when he had sprained his ankle badly on a mountain walk. He would hobble about, come down stairs, get to his study."

Several days later James Cabot Lowell returned. He stayed for tea, found Ralph Waldo greatly improved, and both him and Lydian cheerful. Tentative plans for renting a house in the town were afoot.

"Some day we may even hope to rebuild the old place," Emerson declared, serenely. "If not, we shall find something that will answer."

Mr. Lowell smiled. It was time for him to leave, and as he made his adieus he handed Emerson an envelope.

"Here are the good wishes of a number of your friends, Waldo. They want you to have this personal expression of their sympathy."

"I know I have it, but I'm glad to get their message. Good-bye, and don't worry about us. We shall get on famously." He smiled, and in his clear eyes Lowell could see no shadow of grief, of anxiety.

Back in the parlor he handed the letter to Lydian:

"You read what they say to us, my dear."

She opened the envelope, drew out the inclosure and sat, silent, staring.

"What is it, Lydian?"

"I—I don't know—" she handed him a check. It was drawn for five thousand dollars.

With it was a sheet of paper containing only the well-wishes of a group of his "old friends."

"But I—we can't accept this!" He looked at her, and there was heaven in his face. "We cannot keep this money, my Queen without guile, but we see back of it the white glory of friendship. They love us, Lydian."

"They love you," she murmured. "And who would not love you?"

There was a step outside, a voice in the open door, and Judge Hoar entered to greet his friends. At once Emerson showed him the check:

"You know of this?"

"You'll have to take it, Waldo. If you don't, you'll hurt your friends too badly. Those who have joined in giving it to you are happy to be able to show you, in this simple, direct way, what they think of you, and what it means to them to be able to do you a service."

In the end Emerson was persuaded.

"I have until now stood on my own feet, and I supposed I should be permitted to do so until the end, Sam. To tell you that I am profoundly moved by this evidence of the affection in which I am held is only to realize again how little words can express of human feeling."

The two clasped hands.

At the demand of more distant friends a subscription was opened, unknown to the Emersons, and from far and near came donations from men and women who cherished Emerson, some for long friendship's sake, others for kindnesses done that he had forgotten but not they, many simply because they had heard him speak or read his books, and loved him for what he stood for, what he had given them of the bread of angels. More than three thousand dollars thus flowed in, to be secretly deposited to Emerson's account in the Concord bank. Finally Judge Hoar appeared again, bringing with him the check book.

"You remember how Mrs. Alcott used to say that if you cast your bread on the waters, it would come back to you buttered? Here's the buttered slice, old friend. I've been talking to your distant cousin, W. R., the architect. He tells me there's more money than you need to rebuild your house, and work is to begin at once if you wish it. There isn't a builder in town who isn't eager to give his services simply for the cost of material."

"We can't allow that."

"No, and we needn't. Young Emerson's coming up to see you tomorrow with the plans."

There was nothing niggardly in Emerson, and he could understand and rejoice in the generosity of others. He expressed his joy freely in a circular letter which he gave to James Lowell to pass among those who wished to remain anonymous. To the rest he wrote individually. They had made him a happy man.

When the cost of the reconstruction was figured and the sum laid aside, enough remained to take Ellen and himself on a trip abroad for some six or seven months. By the end of the summer Emerson showed the reaction to all the excitement he had been through. His doctor wanted him to get away, advised a sea trip and a winter in a mild climate. Egypt was agreed upon.

The trip was in every way a success. From the first Emerson's health improved. The aphasia that had become extreme disappeared. Father and daughter stopped briefly in England, saw old friends, Carlyle among them, were joined by Edward, (Edith and her husband having returned at news of the fire), who took them to Paris, where James Russell Lowell was one of the first to call at their hotel. Everywhere Emerson was made much of. He took everything easily, lay late in bed, smiled at Ellen when she wanted to take him sight-seeing, told her to go alone. He smoked an occasional cigar, drove when the sun was bright. They remained a while on the Riviera on their way to Cairo, where they took comfortable quarters. Ellen wrote home delightedly telling of her father's fine health, how even his hair was growing in thick, how homesick he was, how he found friends wherever he went. "Everybody who meets him loves him," she said. In regard to his homesickness she told how, as the steamboat they were on entered the mouth of the Nile, he had stared out on the barren landscape and remarked, with a disgusted wave of the hand:

"My dear, could anything argue wilder insanity than our leaving a country like America and coming all this way to see a bareness of mud, without even an inhabitant?"

She pointed to a few figures moving over the expanse in the distance.

"So there are a few, after all! They must have come to drown themselves."

But he was soon enjoying himself, amused by the strange life, by the new foods, the fruits, the flowers, interested in the great monuments.

It was not until spring was safely back that Ellen would consent to begin the home trek. They paused again in Paris, where the trees were budding along the boulevards and in the parks; and where Taine came to call and to present the distinguished American with his monumental work on English Literature. Another caller was the charming Russian, Turgenev. In London again there were old friends to greet, Carlyle of course, Alexander Ireland, Froude. He met Ruskin, found him very gloomy, Jowett, whom he liked, and Lewis Carroll, of *Alice in Wonderland*. With Ireland he made a trip to the Lakes, but the old poets had vanished. He even made one speech, at the urgent plea of the labor leader, Tom Hughes, before an audience of workingmen at the Workingmen's College. He was enthusiastically cheered at the end, and shook hands with many of the men, two of whom each pressed a golden sovereign into his hand. "Please, Sir. We want more than we can say to have a bit of a hand in helping to rebuild your house."

"And so you shall, my friends," he promised, "and I thank you with all my heart."

On a lovely day in May the two travelers came rattling in to the station at Concord. As the engine rounded the curve and came into sight it let out a long, wild scream. News of Emerson's landing in Boston had been telegraphed to the Court House, and, as agreed upon, the church bells had rung out to let all the neighborhood know, ending by slowly tolling out the hour of his arrival in the town. All the countryside was therefore awaiting him, and as the train drew to a stop and his tall, familiar figure, wrapped in the equally familiar blue cloak, appeared and descended upon the platform, cheer after cheer rose on the air, hats were tossed up, hands waved; slowly, between two long lines of smiling, excited children dressed in their best and scattering flowers, behind whom crowded their elders, he and Ellen walked to the waiting carriage. The band crashed into a march, and following it, the procession moved on through the street, the Square, to the Lexington Road and the Emerson house.

The Emerson house. There it stood, looking exactly as if nothing had ever happened. Green and white, foursquare, benignant, essence of home and peace, it stood under its trees, amid its flowers, and smiled upon the returning master.

Out upon the porch came Lydian.

"Welcome home, my husband."

She led him into the restored house, while outside all his neighbors waited. All was as it had been. His study the same familiar room, with its pictures, its furniture, its books, everything in place, the same deep red curtains, the very bell-cord, all, all!

His face alight, the beloved Sage of Concord stepped out again to thank those who waited. He could not speak. His voice choked in his throat. At length he managed to utter some halting words of affection and blessing. His voice, though broken, reached everyone, for not a sound was made until he ended. Then came one long last cheer, and the crowd departed, leaving him to his family.

Lydian, writing next day to her brother, Dr. Jackson, to tell him of this return, finished the letter with these words:

"If there is a lighter-hearted man in the world I don't know where he lives."

Chapter XVIII

The Goal, well worth the cruise, is near. . .

A HUNDRED years from the day when the Minute Men of Concord fought the opening battle of the Revolution the statue in their honor made by Daniel Chester French, himself a Concord boy, was unveiled on the site where they had stood, across the stream from the old granite shaft, where the British stand had been made. A grim old farmer, Ebenezer Hubbard by name, had greatly resented this mistake in place, as he called it, so much so indeed that he remained away from the celebration, and left, in his will, a thousand dollars to be devoted to a new monument "that shall stand where it should stand."

Emerson was the speaker at the ceremonies.

Those who heard him – and all Concord was there, with old friends come from Boston and other near-by towns – felt it to be a precious occasion. Waldo was completely at home, and spoke with a grace, a depth of feeling, an ease more or less unexpected, for there had been times when his hesitations were painful. Not today, under the shimmering April sunlight, on his ancestral ground, surrounded by those who loved him, whose every face was familiar. The theme, of individual dedication, of individual sacrifice for a great end, was after his heart. And while he praised those long-dead youths, facing the foe, "their flag to April's breeze unfurled," it may have seemed to some in that audience as though he too stood under the shining folds of a greater banner, facing the dark, sad host of all man's inner enemies with the clear faith, the high courage which the long years had but strengthened and tempered for him, stood there in the certainty that defeat was impossible.

During the next four years he made an occasional address, and in 1879, forty years from the date of the famous Divinity School lecture that had so startled all his world, he was again invited to speak to the graduating class. He took as his subject "The Preacher" and made of it a fit finale to the earlier discourse. But there were at moments long pauses, difficult seeking for the word he wanted, an effect of strain that decided the family to make this his last public appearance.

During several weeks of this year Daniel Chester French was occupied in modeling that bust of Emerson which is perhaps the finest likeness ever made of him. Speaking of his sitter's head French said that it had made him remember a remark of Henry James the elder to the effect that the American face tended to be over-modeled. "And it is true that no face was ever more modeled than Emerson's. But there was nothing slurred, nothing accidental; in its perfection of detail it was like the greatest sculpture, for the detail did not interfere with the great scheme."

As for Emerson, looking at the result after each day's labor, he asserted, with that quick glimmer of amusement on his face so characteristic of him:

"Dan, the more it resembles me, the worse it is!"

By one of life's amazing coincidences Emerson found himself, in response to an invitation from the pastor of the Unitarian Church, back in Concord, New Hampshire, fifty years to the day from his wedding with Ellen Tucker. He wanted to see her home again, but on going up the once familiar street found it had disappeared, and that another had been built in its place. The same afternoon Ellen's half-brother, Colonel Kent, called upon him at the parsonage. Emerson mentioned his regret that the old house had been destroyed.

"It has not. Only moved to another street. Come, I'll take you there. I know the people who live in it—they will be honored."

They went. The house was unchanged, even the rooms were as he remembered them. Silently he moved through them; silently, with a grave smile and inclination of the head, he took his departure.

The visit must have held the quality of a dream. That girl and boy, she who had vanished into the grave, he into old age, were they like ghosts to him now?

During the last miles of his life journey there was always, when he was away from home, so we are told by his friend and biographer James Eliot Cabot, an "unknown bodyguard" watching out for him. Everybody knew him. On Boston streets, in a train, some friendly eye saw that he was in no difficulty. Ellen was usually his companion, but he liked to make his visits to Dr. Holmes, to friends in Cambridge or elsewhere by himself. And somehow, unobtrusively, should he appear unsure of his way, uncertain of taking the train, there was a friendly hail: "Are you going our way, Mr. Emerson?"

Often he did not know one of these guides, but all knew him.

During the winter of 1881-82 he resumed a habit, long laid aside, of going to church. Ellen was always with him. Edward, who on his return from Europe had married Judge Keyes' daughter, Alice, was a practicing physician, and made his home with his father, over whose health he kept a watchful eye. In spite of the loss of memory there was nothing feeble, nothing senile about Ralph Waldo. He liked to walk to the post office on pleasant afternoons, he read in his study, was always down for breakfast, and he enjoyed the callers who dropped in on the family. The soul of kindness within him shone ever more clearly in his face as he drew toward the edge of eternity. The hesitant manner, the search for the right word, which, as Holmes had mentioned so long ago, produced an effect suggesting someone crossing a brook on stepping stones, grew more marked, and the word often could not be found. But this was all of age's infirmities to fall upon him.

On a Sunday in mid-April, the sixteenth, he told Ellen he wanted to go to church in spite of the fact that the day was gray and chill, with an inclement wind.

"Hadn't you better stay by the fire, Father?"

But go he would.

Next morning he had a slight, feverish cold. At breakfast Edward asked him if he wouldn't go back to bed until he shook it off, but as always Emerson rebelled at this suggestion. Going to bed always made him feel worse. There was nothing the matter with him but a trifling cold. The day was fine, and a walk in the sun was what he needed.

The cold in fact grew no worse, and for the next three days he went on as usual, spending the evenings with Lydian, taking his short afternoon walk, reading in the morning in the study he loved.

But on the fourth day, coming downstairs with Ellen to the midday meal, he suddenly faltered, giving a slight exclamation of distress. She had her arms about him in a moment, helped him back into his room and got him into bed. He looked at her and murmured:

"I had hoped it would not come like this, Ellen."

"Father, it's nothing. You'll be all right."

And so, it seemed, he was. Late in the afternoon he insisted on getting into a dressing gown and coming down to the parlor, to have tea there with Lydian and the family.

There were symptoms of pneumonia, but Emerson fretted so greatly when his son and daughter tried to insist on his keeping his bed next day that it was thought better to humor him. He dressed each morning and descended to his study, where he spent the day comfortably enough in an armchair before the hearth, with its pleasant woodfire. Now and then his mind wandered slightly. During one of these periods, when he seemed bewildered and not sure where he was, his eyes fell on a portrait of Carlyle. He smiled, and with a glance full of affection, remarked "*That* is that man, my man."

On Saturday evening when bedtime arrived he bent over the hearth to arrange the fire for the night, as he always liked doing. His hand trembled as he separated the smoldering bits of wood with the tongs, but when Ellen would have helped, he waved her gently aside.

As he left the room he paused for a moment, looking back at it. He was never to see it again.

He died on Thursday, April 27, 1882, passing quietly, serenely from this world. For the last three days he had known he was dying, and had asked that the relatives or friends who came to the house to inquire after him should be brought to his room. Of each he took his gentle farewell. On the final day came James Eliot Cabot. Emerson knew him, smiled upon him, tried to say something but was not able to speak.

From far and wide they came, the old and the young, his friends, his admirers, to pay him the last honors. His grave was dug near those of Hawthorne and of Thoreau, and as it had been for them, the day was lovely with budding spring. He had said of Hawthorne's burial that it was more like a happy meeting than a sadness of farewell, and it was so for him. It was the end of an earthly experience, deeply and nobly lived; but it seemed also the beginning of, the advance toward a greater, a richer life.

"O tenderly the God of Day filled his blue urn with fire!"